*Time's running out
on the Sands of Dee*

Time's running out on the Sands of Dee

Peter Ford Mason

Dedicated to the memory of Ellen Shannon,
(younger sister of the author's great grandfather)
who died at age of 14 years on 30 January 1850
at Trimdon Grange Colliery Co Durham.

Article – *Newcastle Chronicle* 8 February 1850:

Ellen was knocked down by a train of coal waggons
on a railway line [between Trimdon and Hartlepool]
one foot and part of her leg was crushed
and her leg was subsequently amputated
but not withstanding she died the following day

2 weeks earlier a boy aged 4 years died
at Ludworth Colliery [Co Durham]
in attempting to cross the railway line was
knocked down by the tender of a locomotive engine

Front cover: Based on the poem 'The Sands of Dee' by Charles Kingsley.
Charles Kingsley (1819–75) was a Christian Socialist promoting working men's colleges and labour cooperatives. As an Anglian he secretly married a Catholic, Frances Grenfell, in 1844. He was appointed Professor of Modern History at Cambridge during 1860–1869 and as Residentiary Canon of Chester Cathedral in 1869. He was a close friend of Thomas Carlyle, author of *Chartism* (published 1839), and Charles Darwin whose book *On the Origin of Species* was published in 1859. Kingsley wrote the *Water Babies* in 1863 which drew attention to the cruel conditions which child chimney sweeps had suffered for many years.

Every effort has been made to trace copyright holders for images used in this book.

First published in 2022 on behalf of the author by
Scotforth Books (www.scotforthbooks.com)

ISBN   978-1-909817-47-0

Typesetting and design by Carnegie Book Production, Lancaster.

Printed in the UK by Halstan

Contents

Illustrations

Engineering v. nature

Solar power as a dominant influence was recognised by the ancient Egyptians in their sun god Ra. Five thousand years later, the power of the sun cannot be ignored! From earliest times animals and humans have battled with nature as they fought for survival and to ensure reproduction. Eventually humans gained power over animals and then made use of animals to increase their advantage over other humans. Hunting 'in packs' led to the general need for collective strength in war and peace.

Development of control over nature started at a primitive level using sensual awareness and then the use of tools, such as levers and wheels; this could be described as the beginning of engineering. The need for food and drink had to be satisfied. Nature provided nourishment in the form of plants, trees and fruit, and water was supplied by rainfall and the moisture absorbed by plants and collected in natural reservoirs, streams, rivers and seas. If water was not readily available, man would dig below ground by hand and with tools when available; later more sophisticated implements would allow shafts to be dug to greater depths.

The engineering techniques in mining were developed early to obtain the materials needed to hunt animals for sustenance and then in warfare to establish superiority between competing groups of humans. Slavery and serfdom were human abuses of power which continued through the ages. Evolution by natural selection was the passing on of experience down the generations by animals and humans.

In military combat, the need for harder materials like metals ensured that mining for copper, silver and iron ore developed firstly at locations where these were readily available. The engineering techniques used in mining then became part of the military machine when men with mining skills were used such as in the siege of fortresses. This led to the production of metal fighting weapons with sharp cutting edges, and then lighter weapons gave greater manoeuvrability in combat. The use of horses (horsepower) was soon adapted in both domestic and military situations. Other animals used have included camels, llamas, elephants, reindeers and dogs; also ostriches and pigeons.

In agriculture the required movement of carts and machinery made use of cattle as well as horses and ponies. The development of transport with other types of power led to the use of water (and steam), wind, canals, and rail using wood, peat, coal, oil, gas and other forms of fuel. As the industrial revolution advanced, many more industries became viable; for example, the availability of cheaper water and rail transport made coal mining a boom industry. Also, the export of heavy goods by sea made industries much more competitive.

Many of the engineering skills developed during the evolution of mining were adopted by the construction industry and armed services such as boring, shaft sinking and blasting. Mining engineers later in their careers were able to take on responsibility for major civil engineering projects, especially where tunnelling and geotechnical experience was needed.

However the mining of fossil fuels has resulted in the significant production of carbon dioxide as a by-product leading to climate warming. Greenhouse gases, which trap the sun's heat, are causing a significant rise in global temperatures. This has made it essential in present times that the means of living and working are fundamentally re-appraised. This inevitably leads to political choices, relating to resources and funding.

The human need for collective protection has developed over the centuries. Following land-bound serfs, the townspeople in the Middle Ages gained more freedom to engage in commerce, and formed groups known as merchant and craft guilds. Craft guilds reached their peak prosperity in the fourteenth cenury. Then from the late eighteenth century to the late nineteenth century, trade unions became established, and legalised from 1824. The fight for democratic rights began with Chartism in the 1830s. Thus from feudalism to the battle between capitalism and socialism; perhaps now to submit to the 'Green Revolution'.

INTRODUCTION

River Dee & estuary siltation

History began to record the importance of the River Dee (Afon Dyfrdwy) at the time of the Romans as they imposed their control over Britain two thousand years ago. They established a stronghold in north-west England by building a military fortress and establishing Chester as one of their principal ports. Chester was then known as Deva Fluvius after the River Diva (Latin for goddess) which discharged nearby into the Irish Sea.

The Dee estuary owes its origin to the passage of glacial ice pushing south-eastwards from the Irish Sea. The inner parts of the estuary were filled by glacially derived sands and gravels. The source of the River Dee is in Snowdonia. Nearby at Lake Bala, Thomas Telford introduced river sluices in the early 1800s. After the village of Corwen, the river passes the Berwyn mountains at the manmade Horseshoe Falls and then on to Llangollen. The river then flows under Telford's Pontcysyllte aqueduct carrying the Llangollen Canal. The River Dee reaches Chester after a total of 70 miles; the lower section of the river has remained a national boundary between Wales and England since 1536. The River Dee (in conjunction with the River Mersey) still plays a crucial function in the North West providing:

Drinking water supply

Transport, means of access and trade links

Fishing – (incl commercial) and other recreational activities

Agriculture – cattle and sheep on the marshlands

Wildlife habitats and Sites of Special Scientific Interest

During recent centuries the main factor which has affected the estuary between North Wales and the Wirral has been the silting of the bed of the estuary. This has had an adverse impact on Chester as a port, and required subsidiary ports or 'outports' to be established further down the estuary to enable goods from larger vessels to be unloaded. Hoylake took over from Meols about 1200 followed by outports on the Wirral coastline starting with Shotwick and Denhall (in 1278), then Burton (1322), Neston (1541) and with anchorages at Parkgate (1700) and Dawpool (1707). When coal mining started at Neston, quays were also constructed at Denhall/Ness (1790) and Little Neston (1873).

By 1850, silting had developed to such an extent, that the export of coal by sea was no longer economic since cheaper coal could be obtained from other collieries. Neston mine owners were forced to consider alternative means for the export of their coal. Rail transport was made available by 1875. Many eminent civil engineers have been employed to explore the means of providing additional channels and canals to increase the estuary water flows and depth. This gave some short-term improvements but tended to worsen the ship access on the opposite side of the estuary. In 1737 a New Cut (5 miles long from Chester to Shotton) was dug on the Welsh side to straighten and canalise the estuary. Even as late as 1817, Thomas Telford was called in to provide advice on lessoning the effect of the continuing silt problem.

In 1847 as the Ness coalfield was coming to a close, a disaster took place at the new Chester Dee Bridge which collapsed with the death of five people. Further sombre news on the Dee was captured three years later by Charles Kingsley in his poem:

The Sands of Dee

'O Mary, go and call the cattle home,
And call the cattle home,
And call the cattle home,
Across the sands o' Dee;'
The western wind was wild and dank wi' foam,
And all alone went she.

The creeping tide came up along the sand,
And o'er and o'er the sand,
And round and round the sand,
As far as eye could see;
The blinding mist came down and hid the land –
And never home came she.

'Oh, is it weed, or fish, or floating hair –
A tress o' golden hair,
O' drowned maiden's hair,
Above the nets at sea?
Was never salmon yet that shone so fair,
Among the stakes on Dee.'

They rowed her in across the rolling foam,
The cruel crawling foam,
The cruel hungry foam,
To her grave beside the sea:
But still the boatmen hear her call the cattle home
Across the sands o' Dee.

Apparently this poem, based on a sketch by painter Copley Fielding, was first published in the book 'Alton Locke' by Kingsley in 1850, in sympathy with Chartism, a democratic movement to promote basic rights for working people. Fielding's sketch pictured at the mouth of the Dee a girl, who in bringing her father's cattle home across the sands, had been caught by a sudden storm and flow of the tide. The next day, her corpse was found, hanging among the fishing stake-nets.

Today walking along the Wirral side of the Dee estuary, it is difficult to imagine that 200 years ago there was an industrial revolution taking place on the Wirral peninsular mainly generated by the coal mining works in the Neston area. The problem with the silting of the estuary (the process of increasing concentration of suspended sediments) adversely affected the flow of water and access by ships and large boats as well as impairing fish and other aquatic organisms.

Engineering works associated with countering the silting of the estuary including its effect on Chester and its outports determined the development of Wirral and North Wales, and the succession of Liverpool as a major British port. On the east side of the Wirral peninsular, the River Mersey also played a major role in the development of Liverpool and Merseyside.

The history of the north-west of England has been intimately connected to the trade with Ireland and the effect of centuries of conflict between England and Ireland. Many of the famines in Ireland resulted in Irish families seeking refuge in Liverpool, and some then gained passage to North America, while other Irish families settled in other parts of England, Wales and Scotland.

This book gives the story of the historical journey of the River Dee, especially the impact of the silting up of the bed of the estuary through consecutive periods of history from Roman up to present times. In the engineering context this includes the story of the roads and fortifications first constructed by the Romans followed by later civil engineering and mining works carried out on parts of the River Dee and its estuary. The evolution of engineering included the development of the means of transport including the use of seas, rivers, canals, roads and railways which were often critical to the financial viability of many industries. Mining prompted the use of different forms of power, including the use of engines fuelled by steam and oil.

However many industries produced horrific working conditions especially in coal mines. During the period of coal mining at Neston between 1759 and 1928, the increased pollution generated by these workings at Neston would have literally spread a blanket of coal dust over a large area around the coal mines. As well as soiling the countryside around the pit head, it would have had a serious impact on the health of all people working and living in this area. The early death of many children at this time is evidence of the adverse effect on health in the local environment around Neston.

Natural resources such as water, wind and sunlight have always been available, but the dangers of global warming have now focused attention on options which do not have harmful consequences for our environment. In the following pages, details are given of engineering actions taken during the main periods of history, and the effect of the natural and man-made impact on sections of the River Dee and its estuary and the implications for the future.

Even today the Dee estuary can be a dangerous place with erosion of coastal banks, shifting sands, strong tidal currents, flooding, and pollution. In 2018 there were flooding incidents at New Brighton, West Kirby and near Gayton due to high spring tides, severe gales and tidal surge. Flooding also occured at Hoylake, Meols, Moreton and Wallasey. Fort Perch Rock car park was subjected to flooding in 2013.

The Environment Agency in England and Natural Resources Wales have worked together to manage flooding on the River Dee and its tributaries. They produced a report on preliminary flood risk assessment in December 2018.

The River Basin District (RBD) Management Plan relates to the area of land drained by the river and its tributaries. The River Dee RBD has a long history of flooding with records dating back to the thirteenth century, and as a whole has suffered significant flooding in 1890, 1946, 1964 and 2000. The part of the Dee RBD in England is at risk from both river and tidal flooding with recent events in 2000, 2007, 2012, 2014 and 2016. The 2007 event was the largest flood in England in recent history.

The Environment Agency (EA) has carried out reent flood assessments in accordance with RBD criteria, drawing attention to the following risk areas:

> River Dee flood embankments in Chester
>
> Sealand main drain flood basin
>
> Finchetts Gutter outfalls and debris screens at Sealand Road
>
> Dee Lock at junction of Shropshire Union Canal and River Dee at Chester

River Dee reservoirs are also at risk of flooding. On West Kirby promenade, piling for the new flood defence sea wall has just started, due to be completed by November 2022.

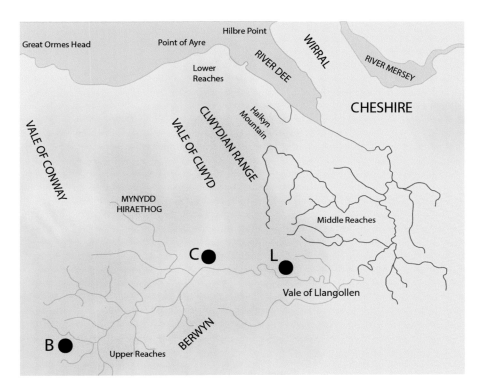

The River Dee and Estuary (showing locations of Bala, Corwen and Llangollen)

Bala

The River Dee rises on the slopes of Dduallt above the village of Llanuwchllyn in Gwynedd, Snowdonia, at a height of 1,220m above sea level near the town of Bala, the site of a first century Roman marching camp. In 1485 Henry Tudor's army marched through the Bala area onto the Battle of Bosworth.

Corwen

Corwen is located on the banks of the River Dee beneath the Berwyn mountains ten miles west of Llangollen. In 1400 Owain Glyndwr, a Welsh leader fighting for Welsh independence, was proclaimed Prince of Wales at Corwen. This town in Denbighshire is well known for coarse fishing.

Llangollen

Llangollen (in Denbighshire) was a religious settlement named after Saint Collen, a seventh-century monk. In the sixteenth century a bridge was built across the River Dee at Llangollen. A weir (Horseshoe Falls) was built 1824–6. The Llangollen (Irish) Ladies attracted many famous visitors to their home Plas Newydd during 1780–1830. Each year since 1947 Llangollen has held an International Eisteddfod, a festival of singers and dancers.

Romans 79–410

Castra Deva (Chester), Wirral and North Wales

One year after Agricola was made Governor of Britain, in AD 79 the Romans established a fort at Chester their major port in the north-west of England. Nearby in Flintshire the Romans carried on the local industry of lead mining and smelting.

There is also evidence that Roman engineers constructed a road running from Chester towards the north of the Wirral peninsular (at a port later known as Meols). Roman remains have also been discovered at various locations in Wirral and Cheshire. The Romans used Meols as a subsidiary deep port up to 937. The earliest record of a build-up of silt around the port of Chester was in AD 383. Nearly thirty years later the Romans left Britain.

Main Port: Deva (Chester), OutPort: Meolse (Meols)

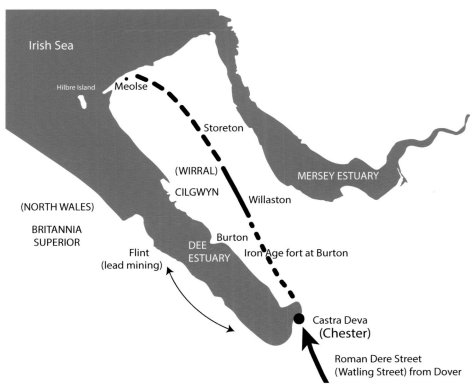

Wirral (Old English wir for myrtle tree, and heal); myrtle was vegetation which covered the peninsular at this time.

Chester was chosen by the Romans in a strategic location at the centre of Roman Britain and was first occupied by their 2nd legion, a unit with naval experience. The city walls were built in AD 70–80 and amounted to an earth embankment with timber palisade fence. Roman campaigns from Chester into Wales was made difficult due to the marsh-lands to the south-west.

A celtic pre-Roman tribe known as Cornovii had occupied a fishing and farming settle-ment beside the bank of the River Dee. Later local people were attracted to the Roman fortress, and were employed as servants and labourers (both free and slave) working within the walls and on the harbour facilities.

The main advantage held by the Roman site was its location at the highest navigation point on the Dee. It also allowed a watch over the tribes Ordovices and southern Brigantes and supervision of lead mining operations in north-east Wales. Preparations were made by the Romans for a possible conquest of Ireland.

Following the arrival at Chester of the 20th legion (XX) after their service in Scotland in AD 90, a decision was made to rebuild the entire depot in stone using readily available local quarries. The main feature now remaining of the Roman presence in the centre of Chester is the stone amphitheatre constructed in the first century (only the north half is still exposed). There are many Roman remains in Chester attracting tourists world-wide, especially the city wall which encircles the present city centre.

The evidence of Roman activity on the Wirral peninsular includes the following:

Hilbre Islands – Roman pottery found

Meols – road to Dove Point near Hoylake indicating a busy trading community; crema-tion urns, coins and skeleton

Birkenhead – remains of a timber bridge found deep in silt below Bridge Street and boathouse

Oxton and Easton – Roman coins

Greasby – signs of Roman Road near Pump Lane

Storeton – signs of sandstone quarrying and packhorse track

Irby – farmstead

Willaston – Roman road close to Street Hey Lane

In AD122 Emperor Hadrian made use of resources from Chester for use in the Roman great frontier works running from the Solway Firth to the Tyne. This transfer of resources curtailed planned re-construction works in the Chester area. Further troubles in the north of England and the need for troops to return back to Rome again frustrated planned activities around Chester.

Artistic view of Deva Victrix. Julian Baum/Take 27 Ltd

Tile antefix with the name of Legion XX and a wild boar, the legionary symbol, from Holt, Clwyd, Wales, second–third century AD. British Museum, London. Creative Commons: AgTigress

Anglo-Saxons & Vikings 410–1066

Chester (Ceaster), Mercia and Wirral (Hundred of Wilaveston)

The Hundred of Wirral (Wilaveston) was founded in the eighth century. Hilbre Island was named after priestess St Hildeburgh who lived there during the seventh century.

After continuing battles between Welsh and Saxon kingdoms, the Saxons further strengthened the fort at Chester against the Danish Vikings who were then based on the east side of England. In the early seventh century AEthelfirth, Anglo-Saxon King of Northumberland defeated the Welsh at the Battle of Chester.

The Norse Vikings (Old Norse vik meaning creek or bay) were first seen on the Dee estuary in the early 900s as raiders arriving in their longboats. Following agreement with the Saxon rulers, the Vikings escaping from the Dublin were allowed to settle on the Wirral. These newcomers merged with the indigenous population, and this is still obvious from the Old Norse place names in many parts of Wirral. For example the name of Irby village denotes an Irish-Viking settlement. The reign of the Vikings and Anglo-Saxons in England came to an end at the Battle of Hastings in 1066.

Main Port: Chester, Outport: Meols

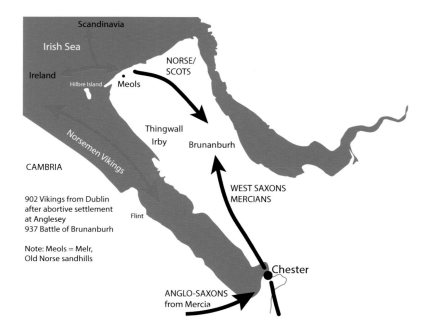

The Viking invaders of the Wirral included Norsemen from the Isle of Man. These invaders set up a parliament at Thingwall (Old Norse – assembly field), a central location on the Wirral peninsular.

Forty years after the fall of the Roman empire in 410, the Anglo-Saxons, a combination of invaders from Jutland in Denmark, Northern Germany, Netherland and Friesland, landed in England. Anglo-Saxon King AEthelred of Mercia in 689 founded the Chester church St John the Baptist which later became the abbey of St Werburgh.

Viking Longship. Image: public domain

Before the Norsemen from Dublin arrived on Wirral's shores the Danish Vikings had invaded the east coast of England establishing their base in York as capital of the Viking kingdom – Danelaw. Alfred became king of the Anglo-Saxons in 871; his first major fight with the Danes (under Guthrum) was between 871 to 875. By 878 most of England (East Anglia and Northumbria) was under Danish Viking rule. For many years there was an uneasy relationship between the forces of Alfred and the Danes.

Viking Invaders. Marshall, Henrietta Elizabeth, b. 1876, Public domain, via Wikimedia Commons

In 902 Norsemen led by Ingimundr, expelled from Dublin and then Anglesey, were given permission to settle in Wirral by Queen AEthelflaed; their settlement was based on farming and fishing. The Saxons apparently did not want to be faced by Vikings on two fronts so avoided being hostile to the Dublin Vikings landing on Wirral.

In 905 after their settlement in Wirral, the Vikings attempted to take the City of Chester but were beaten off by AEthelfaed's forces. The people of Chester are said to have defended the city by pouring hot beer down on the Vikings from the city walls and when the Vikings defended themselves with shields, the defenders hurled down hives of bees. The city was eventually restored in 907. Cheshire became Chester's shire and was known as Chestershire until the fifteenth century.

AEthelflaed, the eldest child and daughter of Alfred the Great, ruled Mercia in the east Midlands from 911. AEthelflaed had a major impact on Chester, by carrying out the re-fortification of the town into a 'burh' and extending the city walls. She promoted the cult of saints Oswald and Werburgh

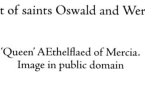

'Queen' AEthelflaed of Mercia.
Image in public domain

of Chester. In 917 her main aim was to establish a line of fortification between Chester and Manchester which required the protection of the Dee Valley and allowed her to harry the Northumbrian Danes.

Anglo-Saxon, Welsh and Viking Kingdoms

In 937 the Anglo-Saxons under Æthelstan destroyed the Norse/Scottish army at the Battle of Brunanburh (widely considered to be Bromborough on Wirral). Olaf Guthfrithson from Dublin combined with Constantine II King of Alba and Owain King of Strathclyde. This conflict was thought one of the most significant battles of the British Isles determining the formation of the English nation.

Normans 1066–1204

Chester

After the invasion by the Normans under William the Conqueror, his magnate Hugh Lupus (the Wolf) was appointed Earl of Chester. Chester was recorded as a settlement in the Domesday Book of 1086. After subduing Cheshire the Normans set to reconstructing Chester Castle in stonework. In 1093 a weir was built near the Old Dee Bridge to maintain the water level for functioning of the adjacent corn mills.

Documents show that in 1190, Liverpool (known as Liuerpul) was an insignificant muddy creek, whereas the port north of Chester at Watergate was flourishing. The Normans still needed to defend Chester against Welsh raids. They saw Chester strategically as a vital 'launch' port for raids against Ireland as well as for trade.

In 1080 on Hilbre Island a church for Benedictine monks was founded by the Normans, and later Hoyle Lake superseded Meols as an outport. In the 1150 Birkenhead Priory and ferry was founded by Benedictine monks.

Main Port: Chester, OutPort: Meols/Hoyle Lake

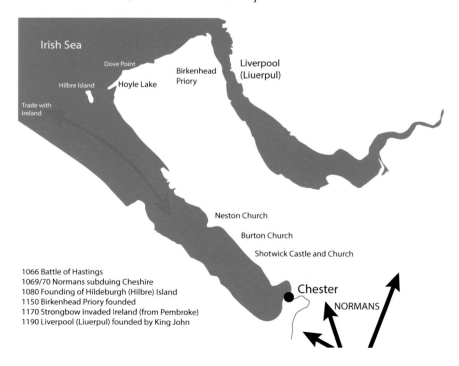

Irish Sea

Dove Point

Birkenhead Priory

Liverpool (Liuerpul)

Hilbre Island

Hoyle Lake

Trade with Ireland

Neston Church

Burton Church

Shotwick Castle and Church

1066 Battle of Hastings
1069/70 Normans subduing Cheshire
1080 Founding of Hildeburgh (Hilbre) Island
1150 Birkenhead Priory founded
1170 Strongbow invaded Ireland (from Pembroke)
1190 Liverpool (Liuerpul) founded by King John

Chester

NORMANS

Norman Soldiers – military advantage in cavalry and archers. Image: duncan1890

Chester Cathedral built 1093–1540 dedicated to St Werburgh. Image: Stephen Hamilton

Middle Ages 1204–1485

During the Middle Ages the world climate became colder and the sea levels began to drop, increasing silting; later retreat of glaciers affected the extent of alluvial deposits.

Shotwick Quay (1278–1471) incl Blacon Point and Saughall

Shotwick Castle motte and bailey constructed by the Normans in 1093 was a defence against the Welsh until 1281. King Henry II left Shotwick for invasion of Ireland in 1171.

At Shotwick in 1278 the River Dee was blocked by a causeway, passable only at high tide. Saughall (Salhale) at this time was a fishing village. The western side of the Shotwick motte acted as a quay and harbour during 1422–71.

1422–71: St Michael's Church at Shotwick, originally a Norman church, was re-built in the fourteenth century.

Main Port: Chester, OutPorts: Shotwick Quay, Burton Quay, Denhall, Hoylake

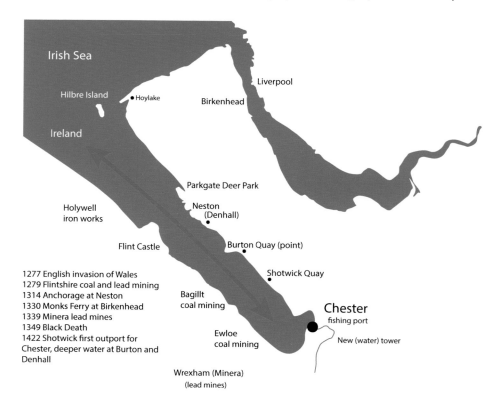

Irish Sea

Hilbre Island

Hoylake

Liverpool

Birkenhead

Ireland

Parkgate Deer Park

Holywell iron works

Neston (Denhall)

Flint Castle

Burton Quay (point)

1277 English invasion of Wales
1279 Flintshire coal and lead mining
1314 Anchorage at Neston
1330 Monks Ferry at Birkenhead
1339 Minera lead mines
1349 Black Death
1422 Shotwick first outport for Chester, deeper water at Burton and Denhall

Bagillt coal mining

Shotwick Quay

Chester
fishing port

Ewloe coal mining

New (water) tower

Wrexham (Minera)
(lead mines)

Liverpool was granted a Royal Charter by King John in 1207. In 1277 and 1283 there were invasions of Wales by King Edward I. In 1303 Neston boats transported forces from Ireland to Scotland for Edward I's campaign to subdue Scotland.

Black Death reached Chester by 1349 with a later outbreak in 1362 causing labour shortages. In 1399 King Henry IV was recorded at Flint Castle.

Chester water tower, by John Skinner Prout.
Gift of J. Byers Hays to the Cleveland Museum of Art

Chester Water Tower
The Water Tower was built between 1322 and 1325, then known as the New Tower.

At this time Chester was a wealthy fishing port but its western location meant that it did not enjoy any significant trade with the continent other than Spain and Germany.

Burton Village. Image: public domain

Burton Quay (1322–1541)

During The Hundred Years' War (1337–1453) a protracted fight for domination between Britain and France involved a succession of rulers on both sides. Burton village

Burton Peg Windmill. Image: public domain

was recorded in the Domesday Book, and once known as Burtone. An Iron Age fort was located at Burton Point (Ness Head), jutting into the Dee estuary and thus provided a natural sheltered harbour. Two ports/quays were established at Burton in the Medieval period, one at the site of a hospital at Denhall and the other at Burton Point.

A peg (mounted on a single vertical post) windmill was built in 1299. St Nicholas Anglican parish church at Burton was first built in the eleventh century, and in 1380 Norman stones were discovered near the church grounds. Quakers were active in Burton from 1663 and a memorial records that Quakers were restricted to burial outside the church-yard.

The coastal saltmarsh at Burton, Neston and Parkgate has provided some feeding for cattle from early times. The saltmarshes which comprise of the upper vegetated portions of intertidal mudflats are usually restricted to comparatively sheltered locations on estuaries. (Burton took a downhill trend in trade after the New Cut was excavated in 1737 and this also affected the ferry service to North Wales.)

In 1806 Burton Manor was purchased from the Bishop of Lichfield by Richard Congreve. The manor was then owned by Prime Minister William Gladstone and in 1908 passed the manor down to his third son Henry Neville (1st Baron Gladstone of Hawarden).

Tudors & Elizabethans 1485–1603

Neston New Quays/New Haven (1541–1743)

The name Neston (Nestone) is of Viking origin with 'ness' meaning a promontory or headland where boats could be docked.

About 1485 King Richard III (and Lord of Ireland) visited Mostyn Hall in North Wales on his way to Ireland. In 1541 consideration was being given to renewal proposals for a new quay at Neston near Lyghtfote Pole. This quay was considered necessary because of the heavy silting up of the estuary around the Burton quay. Before Liverpool was founded, Neston was the largest port in the North West (after Chester) trading with Spain, France and Ireland. At this time the Tudors sought greater control over confiscated land in Ireland.

Main Port: Chester, OutPorts: Burton Quay, Denhall, New Haven (New Quay)

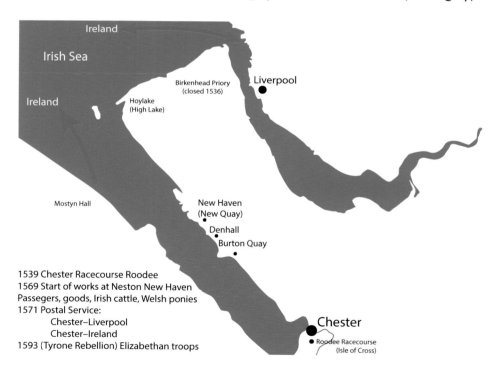

1539 Chester Racecourse Roodee
1569 Start of works at Neston New Haven
Passegers, goods, Irish cattle, Welsh ponies
1571 Postal Service:
      Chester–Liverpool
      Chester–Ireland
1593 (Tyrone Rebellion) Elizabethan troops

St Mary's and St Helen's Church Neston. Image: Rodhullandemu

Henry VIII broke with the Church of Rome in 1534 and Birkenhead Priory closed. The Act of 1540 brought in the legal payment of tithes which was much resisted.

This Anglican Church at Neston was built in the 1100s as recorded in the Domesday Book. It was rebuilt in 1875 as designed by architect J. Francis Doyle using stones of Norman origin. The church also holds some carved stones of Viking and early medieval origin. In addition there are also stained-glass windows designed by Edward Burne-Jones and made by William Morris & Co.

John Wesley, founder of the Methodist Church preached at Neston chapel in 1762. The second oldest Catholic chapel in Wirral, St Winefride, designed by Pugin, was built much later at Neston in 1843. The oldest Catholic church on the Wirral is St Werburgh's at Birkenhead. Both churches have links with rights of ferry – for Neston church across the Dee to Wales and for Birkenhead Priory across the Mersey to Liverpool.

It was rumoured that a smugglers' tunnel was used running from the Old Quay House leading to St Mary's and St Helen's Church.

A 'Friendly Society' was established in Neston to support the less fortunate and to guard against the hardship suffered by working people. A new religious sect, the Free Gospellers, was formed by 97 members who signed a temperance pledge, and later resolved to form a fife and drum band.

Pre-industrial Revolution 1603–1760

The North Wales coal mines started in 1593 and by 1616 were fully productive. In 1748 new shafts were sunk at Latchcraft coalfields near Shotton. The Ness coal mines were an extension of the Flintshire coalfield. Many of the miners at Ness were sought from Flintshire. Starting at this time there were more house chimneys, generating a greater demand for coal. During 1647–48 the plague reduced the population by 40 per cent.

In 1677 the first navigational scheme for a canal between Chester and Flint was proposed by engineer Andrew Jarrington, but this came to nothing. Eventually a new straight channel was excavated near Wales during 1731 to 1736. Nathaniel Kinderley arranged with Netherland engineers to meet at Chester to advise on the construction of this 'New Cut' to breathe new life into the Flintshire shore industries such as coal, lead and lime. The River Dee Company was then formed in 1740 but they neglected the maintenance of the channel allowing it to silt up again. Instead the new company's attention was focused on reclaiming marshlands at Sealand and Saltney.

Main Port: Chester, OutPorts: Denhall Quay, Hoylake, Old Quay (Neston), Parkgate

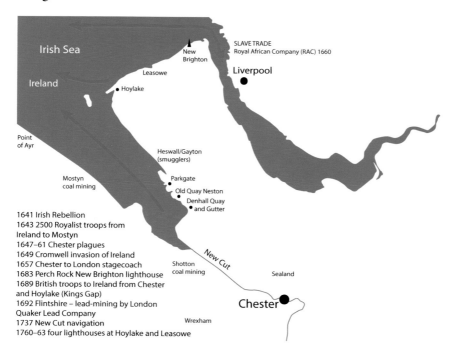

The existing quay at Neston became known as the Old Quay (1743–1804). In 1771 another canal, known as the Denhall or Colliery Gutter, was cut on the Wirral side of the Dee thus widening the river, although ten years earlier engineer James Brindley had considered a canal from Neston to Chester. Neston Quay fell into disrepair before Denhall Quay came into use. The Dee water which used to pass under Flint Castle now moved towards Parkgate.

In 1659 the Battle of Winnington Bridge (Northwich) followed the English Civil War of 1642–1651.

The 'Old Key House' used as an inn located near the quay until 1710, was used as a House of Correction after 1750. As victims of the Poor Law, Irish vagrant women and children were sent there on a temporary basis from Newcastle upon Tyne. Masters of coal vessels were liable to fines if they did not allow vagrants passage back to Ireland. In 1778 Irish vagrants were being accommodated on coal vessels to Newry in Ulster.

The Mostyn family of Flintshire became owners of Great Neston in 1672 and then Parkgate in 1807; they showed great interest in developing the supposed 'Gayton Coal Field' but in the end this did not materialise. Mostyn House School was established in Parkgate town which later was managed by the Grenfell family.

Old Key House at Neston Quays. Image: public domain

Parkgate Anchorage (1613–1820)

In 1245 permission was granted for a deer park at the Parkgate side of Ness. Poachers and their greyhounds caught in the park were severely treated by the 'Forester'. In 1360 the Stanleys had been appointed chief forester based at Storeton Hall. From around 1685, Parkgate acted as a major 'port' up to 1815 with Dawpool anchorage helping out as necessary. Much of the stonework which was demolished at the Old Quay (Neston) was used in the construction of the main wall frontage at Parkgate.

Associated with the marine services at Parkgate, various trades were carried out including boat building and repairing as well as rope-making. A ferry service to Ireland operated from 1686 to 1815. From the 1740s there was a regular ferry service from Parkgate to Flint and Bagillt (North Wales). Celebrities such as John Wesley, Handel and Jonathan Swift sailed to Ireland but often journeys were delayed by inclement choppy waters. By 1820 it was the end of Parkgate as a main port, being too shallow for the Irish (packet) boats.

Bathing at Parkgate became a tourist attraction, even for Lady Hamilton, Nelson's mistress. In 1784 her father Henry Lyons had worked as a blacksmith at Neston coal mine. An open-air swimming pool was built by Mostyn House School in 1923, with filtered salt water supplied from the Dee estuary. A. G. Grenfell, Headmaster of Mostyn School, described the Neston miners' houses as pigsties comparing them with the bright roomy cottages provided by William Lever for his workers at Port Sunlight.

Parkgate Packets. Image: public domain

Parkgate Anchorage Wall. Image © copyright The Francis Frith Collection

For a period during the eighteenth century, Parkgate was an alternative to Holyhead for the Irish packet service. (In 1813 there was a ferry from the Boathouse/Beerhouse to Bagillt.) Liverpool was starting to dominate trading in 1715. In the eighteenth century there was no sea wall or jetty at Parkgate.

Heswall/Gayton anchorage
At the bottom end of the present Cottage Lane, near Gayton Cottage, cattle and other farm animals were brought across by boat from North Wales to Gayton. This service operated over 600 years. Annually a fair was held near Gayton Hall involving such events as folk dancing, cock-fighting and bull-baiting. The owner of Gayton Lane farm was mariner Robert Crabbe whose boats took him as far as Peru. (Robert Stephenson was working in Peru in 1827.)

Heswall beach area was known for anchoring boats. It was considered a 'good birding point' known for flocks of waders, ducks and redshanks. Gayton Gutter became so shallow that sailing activities later moved northwards up estuary to West Kirby.

Heswall and Gayton Smuggling

Heswall also had a reputation for smuggled goods unloaded at night on Heswall and Gayton beaches. The Government was determined to stamp out the 'free-trade' which was organised from the Isle of Man. Irish packet ships were the source of most contraband (including Irish soap) entering Parkgate until the nineteenth century. It was clear that there were underhand dealings between smugglers, landowners, local clergy and 'Preventive Officers' to arrange for temporary storage and later sharing of contraband. There are rock caves near Thurstaston known as the 'dudgeons' which were used for this purpose. The area near Perch Rock, a fortification near New Brighton, also had a reputation for 'wreckers' and smugglers.

A Royal Commission report of the time stated that the Wirral coastline was the 'worst' in Britain for these activities. As early as 1595 a sandstone house near the Wallasey beach called 'Mother Redcap's' was also known for illegal activities. A mounted customs revenue man was stationed at Dawpool to check on smuggling activity on the west side of Wirral. The Government kept a strict eye on the west coast of Britain. Even the poet Robert Burns was employed from 1792 as an exciseman along the Solway Firth (noted in his poem 'The Deil's Awa Wi' The Exciseman').

Early Wirral and North Wales Coalfields

The Flintshire Coalfield stretched from north end at Point of Ayr to the south end at Caegwrie close to Wrexham, and running under the Dee estuary to the Neston area. Early coal mine workings would have existed on both sides of the Dee estuary, but the coalfields in Flintshire started to expand as early as in the sixteenth century.

The period from 1756 to 1763 was known as the Seven Years' War as British and French coalitions battled to obtain supremacy. At that time there was growing competition beginning between Flintshire and Wirral collieries.

The first sign of colliery workings on the Wirral side was in the mid-eighteenth century. Richard Richardson and Rowland Errington were co-owners of Denhall Pit in 1759. Engineer Brindley was involved at this time considering a canal to Chester. Wirral collieries also took legal action due to the diversion of the Dee channel which took almost all of the water away from their coastline impacting on their 'seasale' business. Most of coal exported to Ireland went to Dublin starting in 1761.

First Industrial Revolution 1760–1840

Main Port: Liverpool, OutPorts: Denhall Quay, Old Quay Parkgate, Heswall, Dawpool, Hoylake

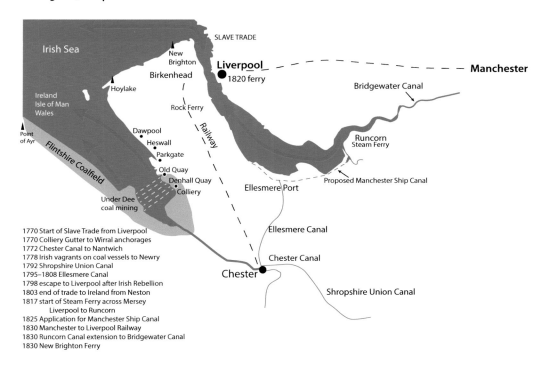

Map labels:
Irish Sea · SLAVE TRADE · New Brighton · **Liverpool** 1820 ferry · Birkenhead · Hoylake · Ireland Isle of Man Wales · Point of Ayr · Flintshire Coalfield · Rock Ferry · Railway · Dawpool · Heswall · Parkgate · Old Quay · Denhall Quay · Colliery · Under Dee coal mining · Ellesmere Port · Bridgewater Canal · Runcorn Steam Ferry · Proposed Manchester Ship Canal · Ellesmere Canal · Chester Canal · Chester · Shropshire Union Canal · **Manchester**

1770 Start of Slave Trade from Liverpool
1770 Colliery Gutter to Wirral anchorages
1772 Chester Canal to Nantwich
1778 Irish vagrants on coal vessels to Newry
1792 Shropshire Union Canal
1795–1808 Ellesmere Canal
1798 escape to Liverpool after Irish Rebellion
1803 end of trade to Ireland from Neston
1817 start of Steam Ferry across Mersey
        Liverpool to Runcorn
1825 Application for Manchester Ship Canal
1830 Manchester to Liverpool Railway
1830 Runcorn Canal extension to Bridgewater Canal
1830 New Brighton Ferry

1776 Talacre new lighthouse, closed 1840s. 1824 Perch Rock lightouse

1825 Post Office 1st steam packet for George IV visit to Ireland from Holyhead. 1830s Steam ferry started from Rock Ferry near Birkenhead to Liverpool

Wirral Coalfields/George Stephenson

In 1770 four times the quantity of coal was exported to Ireland from Ness compared to Liverpool which sourced its coal from Lancashire collieries. It was too expensive for Ness owners to transport their coal to Liverpool.

Many mining engineers and agents from the Tyneside and Durham coalfields were to be employed at the Wirral coalmines. George Stephenson was closely involved in setting up the pit-head plant at Denhall colliery. The appointment of mining engineers from the North East included well reputed viewers (managers) John Buddle and Nicholas Wood. Other 'Geordie' engineers employed were Joseph Cabry, John Henderson, Thomas Storey, John Watson, Robert Johnson and Thomas Roberts.

Denhall Quay (1759–1855) Denna and Snab Pits

As early as 1712 lead and limestone mines using Newcomen engines were in operation at Flintshire. The Stanley family had exploited the coalfields at Bagillt in North Wales from the sixteenth century. So it was no surprise that in 1759 Sir Thomas Massey Stanley began to develop the same coal reserves in the Denhall (or Denna – name of Danish origin) area near Ness.

As in many coalfields, previous work had been carried out on the basis of simple shallow depth pits or drift excavations. There were also lime, tiles and brick works using materials brought back by returning vessels to Ness. Ralph Pearson in 1763, a mining engineer from County Durham was brought in to explore carrying out deeper excavation leading to workings under the River Dee.

From 1770s to 1800 there was a recession in coal mining. The construction of a quay known as Denhall Quay was completed in 1791. Coal was eventually exported by boat to North Wales, Ireland and the Isle of Man, and inland by wagons and via the local canal system.

At this time an underground canal to connect a coal mine at Worsley to Manchester was pioneered by esteemed engineer James Brindley at the Bridgewater Canal. This method of mining was also adopted for the works under the River Dee using 'starvationer' (ribbed) boats. There were two main canals under the Dee, one 350 feet deep and 1.5 miles long, and the other 180 feet deep and 1 mile long (see copy of working plan on page 36).

From 1815, steam power was used on the Dee mining works; Telford was called in by the River Dee Co to investigate deepening of the New Cut which was silting up. In 1835 pit ponies replaced the 'starvationer' boats and 'legger' boatmen to increase the efficiency of coal removal to the pit shafts. Nevertheless by 1850 the Ness mines had financial problems and further silting meant the end of the Denhall Gutter and the Stanley mines. This was not helped by a major financial crisis which took place in Britain during 1825/6 due to a slump in the trade of coal consuming industries.

The suffering of miners' families due to the deaths and injuries down the mines was a feature of the industrial revolution in all coalfields. Apart from 'pitch and toss', cock-fighting and horse racing, the miners' main recreations were drinking and gambling. About 1800 a small pub named the Welch Harp was built for the miners at Denhall close to the quay. The Hinterton Arms (or Shewsbury Arms), Golden Lion, The Malt Shovel, The Brown Horse and the Wheatsheaf at Ness were also popular with miners.

A terrace of seven colliery houses (named Seven Row) was built just inland of the Harp typical of Durham colliery cottages; however most of the miners' shacks were described as 'the most miserable mass of hovels on the Wirral'. It was not until 1872 that the Lancashire and Cheshire miners had a permanent relief society providing some compensation for widows and families of those affected by mining accidents.

Starvationer Boats at Denhall Colliery

These were narrow boats with strong prominent internal timber ribs designed to navigate through the narrow coal mine canals under the Dee estuary as used at the Worsley mines

Bridgewater Canal/Worsley mine/NCB inspector legging. Source: Michael Ware Image Collection

Bridgewater Canal/Worsley mine/NCB inspection party in a starvationer boat.
Source: Michael Ware Image Collection

near Manchester. The miners laid on their backs in these boats and propelled the boat by pushing their legs against the roof of the canal tunnel.

The canal construction workers were called 'navvies' after the man-made navigations which they excavated, blasting through earth and rock.

Canals around Chester

'Canal Mania' was a period of canal construction during 1790 to 1810 until steam loco-motion commenced.

In 1770 the Chester Canal was originally planned as a rival to the Trent & Mersey Canal which was then under construction. The original Chester Canal was constructed to run for 20 miles from the River Dee near Sealand Road to Nantwich in south Cheshire in 1772 and eventually opened in 1779.

In 1796 a new canal from the River Mersey to Chester was proposed to meet the competition from the Lancashire coalfields. This would have involved a link from Chester to Middlewich with a branch to Nantwich, however the Trent & Mersey company were unco-operative about the junction with Middlewich.

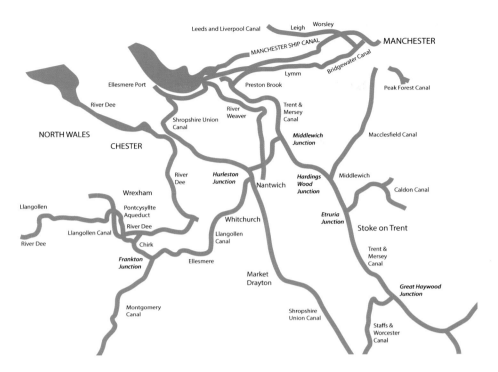

Leeds and Liverpool Canal
Leigh Worsley
MANCHESTER SHIP CANAL
MANCHESTER
Lymm
Bridgewater Canal
Ellesmere Port
Preston Brook
Peak Forest Canal
River Dee
Trent & Mersey Canal
River Weaver
Shropshire Union Canal
NORTH WALES
Middlewich Junction
Macclesfield Canal
CHESTER
River Dee
Hurleston Junction
Hardings Wood Junction
Middlewich
Nantwich
Caldon Canal
Wrexham
Llangollen
Pontcysyllte Aqueduct
Whitchurch
Etruria Junction
Stoke on Trent
River Dee
Llangollen Canal
Chirk
Llangollen Canal
River Dee
Frankton Junction
Ellesmere
Trent & Mersey Canal
Market Drayton
Great Haywood Junction
Montgomery Canal
Shropshire Union Canal
Staffs & Worcester Canal

Canals around Chester

Shropshire Union Canal

After the completion of the Bridgewater Canal in 1761, James Brindley became the chief engineer for the Liverpool and Birmingham Canal which came to be known as the Shropshire Union Canal in 1793. This canal was the last major project by Thomas Telford. It was completed in 1835 stretching 39 miles from Staffordshire and Worcester to Ellesmere and Chester Canal at Nantwich and then linking to the Manchester Ship Canal. Its main function was to transport lime for agricultural use and coal to fire lime kilns. The Trent & Mersey Canal ran from Derby to Runcorn.

Ellesmere Canal

Works on the Ellesmere Canal lasted from 1795 until 1808. By 1804 the Ellesmere Canal Company were still unable to complete the 17 mile gap from Chester to the Pontcysyllte Aqueduct near Llangollen. Two years later the Ellesmere link was completed joining Chester canal to the Ellesmere Canal. The original intention was to extend the Shropshire Union Canal from Trevor (near Llangollen) to Chester as part of a grandiose scheme to link Liverpool with Bristol, but this was never fulfilled.

North West England Slave Trade

After Parliament ended the London-based Royal African Company official monopoly in England in 1698, private merchants in London, Bristol and Liverpool entered the slave trade. In the 1720s Liverpool merchants increased their participation in this line of traffic. Liverpool became the European capital of the slave trade from the 1780s to 1807.

The principal ports of north-west England involved in slave trading were Liverpool and Lancaster. William Davenport from a Cheshire family was owner of the largest number of slave ships based in Liverpool from 1700 to 1808.

In 1761 a John Evans aged 27 who died on a Jamaican plantation, was a Neston owner of a slave ship named 'Neston'. About twenty-five years later the slave trade abolitionist Thomas Clarkson travelled first to Chester and then Liverpool where he inspected samples of iron instruments of torture used on slave captives. Northern Methodist congregations and Quakers were strongly opposed to slavery. During the eighteenth century there was a busy boatyard near Parkgate Boathouse and another at Neston Old Quay. At least one of these boatyards was involved in the African slave trade.

In 1781 on the slave ship *Zong*, 130 African slaves were thrown overboard on the instructions of Liverpool based ship owner William Gregson to avoid payment of insurance claims. This massacre was captured by artist Turner in his painting:

'The Slave Ship 1840', by J.M.W. Turner. Museum of Fine Arts, Boston

Beilby Porteous – Bishop of Chester

Beilby Porteous (1731–1809) who was to become a s stong abolitionist of black slavery strangely was the youngest child of Robert Porteous, a Virginia planter in America. Beilby's early strong views and disdain of tyranny were shown when in 1759 he won the Seatonian Prize for his poem, Death: A Poetical Essay:

> Ah! Why will Kings forget they are men?
> And Men that they are brethren? Why delight
> In human sacrifice? Why burst the ties
> Of Nature, that should knit their souls together
> In one sot bond of amity and love?

As a domestic chaplain to the archbishop of Canterbury in 1762, he became more aware of the conditions of enslaved Africans in the American colonies and the British West Indies. He received reports from early abolitionists Rev James Ramsey and Granville Sharp.

Porteous was appointed Bishop of Chester in 1777 and very quickly came to terms with a vastly growing population at many new centres of Industrial Revolution in the north west of England. There was appalling poverty and deprivation amongst the immigrant workers, pariularly in the manufacturing industries. He took deep interest in the plight of the West Indian slaves; he became involved in preaching and campaigning actively against the slave trade and taking part in many debates a the House of Lords, becoming a noted speaker in this area of social concern.

He had a particular interest in the affairs of the Society for the Propogation of the Gospel in Foreign Parts, with a role in the administration of the plantations in Barbados where 300 slaves were owned by the Society. He criticised the role of the Church of England in ignoring the plight of slaves, particularly in Barbados.

He became a leading advocate for the abolition of slavery, lending support to William Wilberforce, Granville Sharp, Henry Thornton and Zachary Macauley to secure the eventual passage of the Slave Trade Act 1807.

Prime Minister William Gladstone

Gladstone was born at Hawarden in Flintshire. Gladstone's father owned 2508 slaves in British Guiana and Jamaica. His early views on slavery mirrored those of his father, and he wanted to improve the condition of slaves before they were liberated. In 1833 he accepted emancipation, but during the American Civil War he believed that the slave trade could be ended by persuasion rather than by force. In 1898 Gladstone stated that compensation should be given to all slave families.

George Stephenson played a critical role in the early 1800s in modernising Denhall Pit using the latest technology developed in the North East and North Wales. Steam engines pioneered by Cornishmen Savery and Newcomen were already in use in the Flintshire coalfield and Stephenson had visited the Welsh mines and was keen to extend their use to Neston.

In 1815 Stephenson was developing his safety lamp but records suggest that he considered the use of his lamp in Flintshire as unsuitable on the basis that the region's coalfield was not 'fiery', that is explosive gases like methane were absent. However Neston records of mine deaths included miners 'killed in a sulphurous explosion' in 1777 and 1779.

Records also indicated that the early draining methods at Denhall Colliery made use of 'horse-gins'. This method involved the use of horses at the top of the pit shaft; these horses walked along a circular track to turn an en[gin] or gearing mechanism. A few decades later steam engines were available to remove the water from the mine.

By 1825 Stephenson was working in the Liverpool area carrying out preliminary surveys for a rail connection from Chester to Liverpool followed by the major public railway project – the Manchester to Liverpool Railway to carry both passengers and freight. Stephenson made visits to Storeton on the Wirral to inspect the stone quarries for the sourcing of materials for his major project.

Denhall Quay–stone wall remains. Image © Copyright John Slater

Welch Harp miners' public house. Image: public domain. Burton and Neston History Society

With George Stephenson's great practical knowledge of coal mining it was not surprising that he arranged for mining engineers he knew from the North East to be transferred to Neston to set up the pithead machinery. This was the case for Joseph Cabry who had already worked at the Flintshire coalfield. Cabry and his sons Thomas and Joseph were to work at Neston up to the 1880s. The Cabry family were also employed at the Wheatsheaf pub at Ness which many miners frequented.

During the period 1820 to 1850 there was a bitter dispute between the mine-owning family, the Stanleys at Denhall, and the adjacent mine-owning family, the Cottinghams at Little Neston. This resulted in underground assaults between the opposing mine workers leading to long drawn-out court battles. Reluctantly, some of the mining engineers employed from outside areas became embroiled in these disputes; for example Newcastle engineer John Henderson felt unable to support his employer Thomas Stanley at this time. Even George Stephenson felt the need to try and soothe troubled waters!

The safety record at the Denhall Colliery was similar to most coal mines at that time. The working shifts for many mine workers including children totalled over 100 hours per week. The death records revealed that a high percentage of children did not reach the age of 12 years due to injuries down the mine combined with the punishment from working in dangerous levels of coal dust. The later introduction of mechanical cutting tools at the coal face created higher levels of dust and increased numbers of miners with pneumoconiosis, 'black lung disease'. The Dee water was also black!

Pit Shafts at Neston

At the beginning of mining works (after preliminary boring to check depth and quality of coal), sinkers were specialised miners who excavated the shafts from ground level down to the coal seams. As the shaft went deeper, they had to deal with inflow of water, which required particular skills and machinery to keep the shaft dry.

Miners including children died working and travelling in the shafts at Neston Collieries:

1769 John Burroughs – fall into coalpit (shafts were often called pits)

1777 Robert Williams, collier – falling into coal pit

1794 William Griffiths – fell into coalpit

1799 Ellis Kendrick, 65, engineer – falling to bottom of fire engine

1802 Ann Jones, 10 – died from scald in water from colliery engine

1814 Thomas Bartley, 9 – basket's rope broke while descending

1838 James Lewis, collier, 38 – fell from basket while descending shaft

1876 Isaac Fisher, pit sinker, 62 – killed when shaft scaffolding gave way

1877 David Alexander, pit sinker, 24 – hit by object causing fall down shaft

A Government Commissioners Report on mine safety was issued in 1842. The following Act restricted boys working down mines to those over the age of 10 years and banned all women and children from working down mines; often these regulations were not implemented.

Hazel-rod wicker baskets (known as corves) were also used to carry miners and materials up and down shafts; metal tubs and cages were introduced later. The Coal Mines Regulation Act 1860 improved safety rules for workers underground and raised the minimum age limit for boys working down mines to 12 years.

Sketch of children descending mine shaft. © National Coal Mining Museum for England

As a small child living at Wylam near Newcastle, George Stephenson was given the job by his father to keep a close eye on young children playing on the wagon-way in front of his house to ensure that the 'bairns' were not run over by the large coal chauldron wagons passing by.

George Stephenson continued to be concerned for safety at work, and went on to invent a miner's safety lamp (known by North East miners as the 'Geordie'). Miners knew the importance of relying on each other down the pit and therefore always remained a strong community.

The 1851 census for Ness Colliery gives a picture of the working and living conditions in Neston parish as the coal mine at Denhall pit started to wind down.

Littlemore family

The head of a Neston household, Joseph Littlemore aged 68, was given as 'pauper' previously a coal miner. It was not unusual for miners to work past the age of 70 years unless injured or physically unfit. If they were not supported by their family then as paupers they were admitted to the workhouse. The Wirral Poor Law Union formally came into being on 16 May 1836; the earliest workhouse in the Wirral was located at Clatterbridge. The census listed in the colliery housing a total of eight paupers mainly widows. One of these widows, Mary Toole, was born in Dublin.

Joseph's wife Margaret aged 65 was recorded as a cockle gatherer – shellfishing was then a local occupation. Next door neighbour George Peers aged 58 from Puddington was working as a fisherman. Eldest son Joseph Littlemore aged 24 was a coal miner and was the main wage earner for the family. The younger sons John and William worked as agricultural labourers.

Also close by was a person named as 'Not Known' and described as a 'Vagrant – slept in cabin'.

Other occupations recorded at Ness Colliery were brick & tile makers and a basket maker (these baskets were used for carrying miners, tools and coal up and down the mine shafts). The census also recorded the two occupants of a sloop (one-masted sailing boat); the sloop was named Mary (perhaps Mary who lost her life on the Sands of Dee). William Griffiths at the age of 28 was the Master of a Coasting Vessel lying off Ness Colliery. His 'mate' Thomas Davies was 20. They both were born in Bagillt Flintshire which had a ferry service with Neston at that time.

Other census records illustrated local occupations:

Thomas Williams	41	Brick and Tile Maker	b. Neston
Thomas Sharp	46	Basket Maker	b. Little Neston
Thomas Rimmer	29	Gamekeeper	b. Formby, Lancs
James Pemberton	43	Catholic Priest	b. Chorley, Lancs
Alice Basley	34	Fish Woman	b. Ness
James Woodward	47	Schoolmaster of writing and arithmetics	b. Liverpool
Samuel Taylor	65	Well Sinker	b. Neston
John Shannon	30	Gardener	b. Backwood, Leighton Cheshire

In contrast the 1851 census recorded some other residents living at Denhall:

Stanley family of Neston

The head of household was Charles Stanley aged 64, born in Puddington, younger son of late Sir Thos S. M. Stanley Bart; Charles's wife Barbara aged 40 was born in Talacre Flintshire was daughter of Sir Edward Mostyn Bart. Also included were three daughters, and the following staff:

Martha Williams	26	governess	b. London
Martha Williams	52	housekeeper	b. Paddington
Edith Kemp	25	Lady's maid	b. Childer Thornton
Mary Dougherty	30	cook	b. Liverpool
Jane Beeson	19	laundry maid	b. Acton Burnam
Ann Robins	19	house maid	b. Ness
Elizabeth Tusdale	24	nurse	b Sunderland
Cicely O'Conner	20	kitchen maid	b County Mayo Ireland
Benjamin Cotterell	17	footman	b. Ness
Thomas Ashton	31	groom	b. Burton

Gregory family at Neston

James Gregory aged 64 born in Hughton Lancs was Colliery Proprietor employing 120 men, Clerk to the Wirral Union and Superintendent Registrar, and his son Peter aged 18 Colliery Clerk and Bookkeeper.

Cottinghams at Little Neston

Thomas Cottingham	65	Lieutenant Army (half pay)	b. Liverpool

Brocklebanks at Heswall

Thomas Brocklebank	48	Cotton Broker	b. Liverpool

(The Cunard Line was part of the Brocklebank shipping company)

Second Industrial Revolution 1840–1925

Main Port: Liverpool, Outports: Denhall/Little Neston Quay, Dawpool, Hoylake

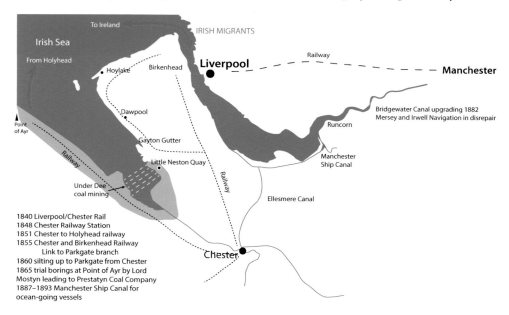

The Potato Famine 1845 to 1849 increased the emigrant Irish population in Liverpool from 17 per cent to 22 per cent. The Irish then further emigrated to the USA and Canada.

Little Neston 'Short Quay' (1873–1928)

The Cottinghams and Earl of Shrewsbury who owned the neighbouring area of Little Neston, initially allowed the Stanleys to extend their workings into the Cottingham area. The Cottinghams started coal mining independently in 1819. The Denhall Quay continued in use for all coal mined. From 1829 when the Cottinghams were exploiting coal in their own area of Little Neston, they arranged for their mine, the construction of a small quay (where a shaft has been sunk in 1875) about 180 yards north of the bottom of Marshlands Road. A foreman pit sinker Isaac Fisher was killed when scaffolding in a shaft gave way. Another pit sinker David Alexander was killed a year later. In Neston Church cemetery the headstone for Isaac uses the word 'killed' indicating his relations considered his death as not accidental.

The Stanley family had been long-standing Roman Catholic with links back to the first Chief Forester of Wirral based at Storeton. In the late eighteenth century, working men's religion was generally Non-Conformist; a Baptist church was founded near the Harp pub in 1908 (closed in 1926). It is not clear whether the impact on the provision of education by the colliery owners benefitted the worker's children. Due to the general anti-Catholicism, the Stanleys would not have openly sponsored schools.

There was a continuing dispute between the Stanley and Cottingham owners which led to sabotage below ground and legal disputes in court, and much bad feeling. A mining engineer from County Durham, Matthew Bates, was working at the Neston mines from 1854, probably to investigate by boring the potential for new mines towards Parkgate. All mining stopped between 1855 and 1873 when new borings were being carried out in the Little Neston area. New colliery houses were built at New Street. The new colliery was re-named as The Wirral Colliery.

A railway, the Mineral Railway Line, was contracted out to the famous Wirral locomotive engineer Thomas Brassey in 1873 to supply a rail connection running from the estuary end of Marshlands Road to the Hooton/Hadlow/Parkgate line. A colliery locomotive, named the Lord Talbot, was purchased from Black, Hawthorn & Co of Gateshead (Co. Durham) in 1881.

In 1866 there was an outbreak of cholera at Neston. This may have originated from the North East where cholera first came to England in 1831 via the port of Seaham at Sunderland. In 1878 water from old workings flooded the mine at Little Neston, forcing it to be abandoned temporarily. Four years later nine pit ponies were drowned in another underground flood at this pit. In 1884 a strike of all miners for higher wages took place in line with general increased trade union activity; this resulted in some men intending to move to the Lancashire collieries. Some miners were charged with gambling at the Harp pub and assaulting the colliery under-manager. In 1889 daily-paid men and pony drivers went on strike for a pay increase to match the wages of piece-rate workers.

Associated with the pithead buildings and plant were the brickworks, tiling and fertiliser works using imported limestone. Adjacent the 'hovels of Wirral' some fields were still used to grow fodder for the colliery horses.

During WWI the British Government took over control of Wirral Colliery. This colliery struggled on until 1925 but petered out due to a combination of poor quality coal and the general industrial disputes leading to the General Strike of 1926. The Wirral coal industry never recovered.

The 'Durham Ox' pub in Ness closed in 1928.

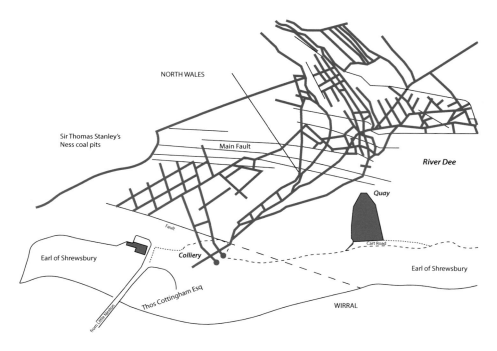

Neston Coalfield under Dee – working plan (showing Little Neston Quay)

Dawpool (Redbank Thurstaston) Anchorage

Anglo-Irish satirist Jonathan Swift landed at Dawpool from Dublin in 1707 en route to Parkgate. In 1822 Telford proposed a canal connection from Dawpool to Wallasey. Other famous engineers were involved in similar proposals included James Brindley, John Rennie, and North East engineer William Chapman who in 1825 put forward a Ship Canal scheme from Dawpool to Manchester without success.

In 1857 another proposal was under consideration for a canal from Dawpool to Chester via Heswall. (At this time the Suez Canal was under construction from the Mediterranean to the Red Sea as the shortest trade route between Europe and Asia).

In 1877 Thomas Ismay shipowner (White Star Line) purchased Dawpool House and later named a vessel *Dawpool*. During the nineteenth century, customs officers were stationed at Dawpool. The White Star ship *Titanic* was built at Belfast in 1909.

Hilbre Islands

The three Hilbre islands are situated at the mouth of the Dee Estuary. They have been occupied since the Stone Age and then as a hermitage before the Norman invasion. An Anglo-Saxon holy woman St Hildeburgh lived at Hilbre during the seventh century. The last monk left in the year 1550.

Hilbre Islands/Liverpool Bay. Image: Peter Craine, geograph.org.uk

A sand dune bridged the gap between the islands and the Wirral peninsular, providing a deep mooring for boats. This facility gradually reduced during the nineteenth century due to silting of Dee estuary when trade switched to the River Mersey. On the Welsh side of Liverpool Bay was Point of Ayr colliery which worked from 1880 to 1996. A lighthouse was built in 1776 at the nearby village of Talacre to give warning to ships using the waters between the Dee and Mersey estuaries. The lighthouse was de-commissioned in 1844.

Hilbre Islands are under protection as a Marine Protection Area (MPA).

Hoylake 'Quay'

The Romans had established a small port (Hyle Lake) near Meols which had a natural deep harbour, and were believed to have had an observation post on Hilbre Island. Salt was a major export at that time. By 1690 the old quay at Hoylake was in decline. King William of Orange and Queen Mary stayed at Gayton Hall at the invitation of landowner William Glegg prior to their crossing at Kings Gap in Hoylake with 10,000 troops to Ireland.

Two lighthouses were constructed in 1763 at Hoy Lake, designed by civil engineer Robert Stevenson. In collaboration with Telford a canal to run up to Wallasey Pool was considered. A lighthouse at Leasowe was constructed at this time to guide ships to Liverpool. By 1900 a seawall extended along nearly the whole of Hoylake's north coast, but by 1908 the quay was put out of use due to silting.

New Brighton

The church of St Peter, St Paul and St Philomena was completed in 1935. It became known locally as the 'Dome of Home' because of its elevated location – the church's dome became a landmark for ships entering the mouth of the River Mersey,

Birkenhead

Birkenhead Priory, the oldest building on the Wirral, was founded in 1150. Monks were granted ferry rights by Edward III; the monks ensured the safety of ferry travellers for next 400 years. From the 1840s, Birkenhead began to prosper with the massive expansion in iron shipbuilding initiated by William Laird. In 2021 the RRS vessel named *Sir David Attenborough* built by Cammell Laird (1829–1947 ironworks) at Birkenhead was launched for climate change and polar research.

Liverpool

The town remained small until its main trade with Ireland started in the early 1500s. Liverpool gained financially from the black 'slave trade' from 1699 to 1862. The American civil war in 1862–63 had a severe impact on the cotton trade.

George Stephenson was appointed Chief Engineer for the Manchester to Liverpool Railway in 1828. During the opening of this first passenger railway in 1830, William Huskisson, a British minister of Parliament, was accidentally killed by a passing train. In the 1840s Liverpool took over from Chester as the main port in the North West with its greater depth of water; growing competition started between Birkenhead and Liverpool. Also the Irish 'Potato Famine' was a major reason for the increase in Liverpool's population providing a home for starving migrants.

The Dee Regulation Scheme (2006) was designed to satisfy Liverpool's increased demand for drinking water supply from the River Dee (also for Birkenhead in 1920).

Miners at the end of their shift at Little Neston colliery.
Image: public domain. Burton and Neston History Society

Merseyside Tunnels and River Mersey

In 1927 engineering consultants Mott Hay Anderson designed the rolling bridge over the River Dee at Queensferry, and the Tyne Bridge at Newcastle in 1928, and four years later the Sidney Harbour Bridge (Australia) in 1932.

The first Liverpool road tunnel (Queensway) was completed in 1934 under the control of chief engineer Basil Mott. He had trained as a junior mining engineer at the Neston collieries in 1882. The Kingsway Tunnel opened in 1971. The Dee Estuary Bridge was built in 1999 over the River Dee near Shotton and Connah's Quay.

Wirral Railways

1830 Chester & Birkenhead Railway – survey by George Stephenson.

1837 Chester to Hoylake construction started using 900 navvies and 40 horses.

1840 Chester to Birkenhead (first railway on Wirral peninsular).

1840–50 North Wales Coast Line Chester to Holyhead.

1847 Act Rail Birkenhead to Holyhead line was opened.

Coal wagons at Little Neston colliery. Image: public domain

During the Chester and Birkenhead rail works in 1839–40 navvy fights necessitated the calling out of the military. Also in 1847 troops were called out from Chester where there was a 'navvy' riot which involved those working on the railway works.

1847–48 rail connection to Lancashire and Cheshire Railways.

1863 Hoylake to Birkenhead, Secombe to Hoylake.

In 1864 the Mersey Railway including tunnel was opened providing direct connection between Birkenhead and Liverpool. [In 1886 construction of railway tunnel was completed requiring 1400 men and 177 horses.]

1866 Hooton to terminus at Parkgate (intermediate stations Neston & Hadlow Road).

1873 Mineral Railway Line (Little Neston to Moorside Lane).

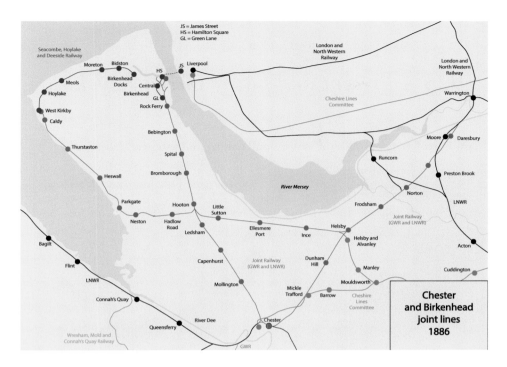

Wirral/North Wales Railways 1830–86

1883 Bidston to Hawarden Dee extension line.

1884 Wirral Railway Co – including Mersey Railway Tunnel with connection to:

New Brighton, West Kirby, Chester & Ellesmere Port.

1886 Parkgate extension to West Kirby including Heswall and Thurstaston.

Mersey Railway Tunnel designed by Charles Fox

Railway Crewe–Chester–Holyhead for Irish traffic

Dee Bridge collapse rectified by May 1847

Menai Bridge – Llanfair to Holyhead line opened August 1848

Britannia Bridge completed August 1858

1925 – Present and future Green Revolution

Main Port: Liverpool, Wirral West: small fishing and safety anchorages

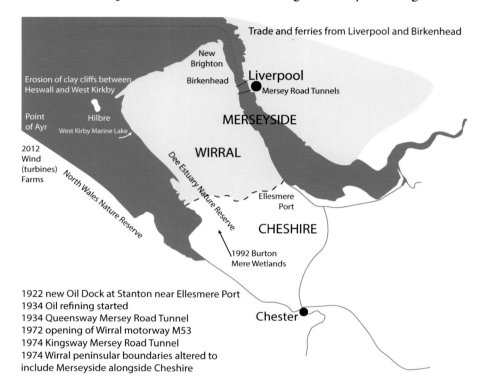

Trade and ferries from Liverpool and Birkenhead

New Brighton

Erosion of clay cliffs between Heswall and West Kirkby

Birkenhead

Liverpool

Mersey Road Tunnels

Point of Ayr

Hilbre

West Kirby Marine Lake

MERSEYSIDE

2012 Wind (turbines) Farms

North Wales Nature Reserve

Dee Estuary Nature Reserve

WIRRAL

Ellesmere Port

CHESHIRE

1992 Burton Mere Wetlands

Chester

1922 new Oil Dock at Stanton near Ellesmere Port
1934 Oil refining started
1934 Queensway Mersey Road Tunnel
1972 opening of Wirral motorway M53
1974 Kingsway Mersey Road Tunnel
1974 Wirral peninsular boundaries altered to
include Merseyside alongside Cheshire

Welsh side of Dee estuary

Shipbuilding along Welsh ports started after the New Cut was completed in 1737 and lasted until the 1960s. Many industries are now closed;. Production at Broughton of Airbus A380 from 2007 for 12 years; wings were barged via Mostyn Docks to France (last delivery March 2021). Largest coastal towns include Saltney, Queensferry, Shotton, Connah's Quay, Flint, Bagillt, Holywell, and Mostyn. RSPB based at Point of Ayr supervises the reserve along the North Wales side of the estuary.

Wirral side of Dee estuary
By 1960 Parkgate, Gayton and Heswall Gutters were choked after ten years of marshland growth. Currently RSPB supervises the marshland reserve from Chester to Heswall.

On 1 April 1974 the Metropolitan County of Merseyside was formed to include the north part of the Wirral peninsular, consisting of Wallasey, Birkenhead, Hoylake, West Kirby and Bebington constituencies, which were formerly part of Cheshire. The Lancashire Metropolitan Boroughs included Knowsley, St Helen's and Sefton. In 1986 Merseyside lost its administrative powers and the constituent boroughs became autonomous administrative units.

Wind farms constructed near Liverpool Bay
2005: 25 turbines Siemens Wirral Power (Burbo) off Wallasey 3.6MW

2016–17: 32 turbines Siemens North Hoyle off Prestatyn 8.0MW

Great Float development near Birkenhead
This is a body of water on Wirral peninsular formed from natural tidal inlet, the Wallasey Pool split into two loarge docks, East and West Floats, as part of Birkenhead Docks complex.

River Dee Tidal Bore
On Dee Estuary there is a tidal bore (created between ebb and flood) 16km long up to the large weir at the centre of Chester. River Mersey also has a tidal bore.

River Dee and estuary – future challenges & regulations

Power, Insulation & Water Supply

Wind Farms – removal of nuclear (fission) power and radioactive waste, and development of non-fossil fuel power; improved building insulation and heat pumps: and solar power

Tidal Lagoon proposed by Mostyn SeaPower Ltd in Dee estuary off Flintshire

Supply drinking water to Liverpool and Wirral, management of reservoirs and sluices

Wildlife including Fishing

Saltmarshes at Burton Point and estuary-management by RSPB of wetland wildlife, grazing, and mud and sandflats not covered by seawater at low tide; Spartina grass was introduced near Shotton steelworks to stabilise marsh; this and other grass have spread as far as Hoylake beach – presently under consideration by Natural England.

North Hoyle Offshore Wind Farm from the beach at Prestatyn Wales. Image: Kaly99

Wading Birds at Burton Mere Wetlands. Image: Paul Jubb

Cockle fishing Dee Estuary Fishery (2008) Management Plan; pearl mussels

Atlantic salmon and trout fishing regulated by Dee District Salmon Fishery Board

Catch & Release angling and prevention of netting to stop salmon exploitation

Coarse fishing Rules (angling for freshwater fish) – at Dee lower reaches

Joint Nutrient Study sponsored by DEFR and MAFF

Sustainable fishing by 2030 under protection of World Seas UN Regulations

Fish Legal environmental angling organisation – sewage pollution

Water Resources Regulation Authority NGO Ofwat

Dee Estuary designated European Special Area of Conservation SAC & SPA

Research, Monitoring, Protection and Enforcement

Environment Agency – access to areas of Site of Special Scientific Interest SSSI

Natural England and Natural Resources Wales (NRW)

Catchment based approach (CaBA)

Continuous Emissions Rate Monitoring System (CERMs)

Water Protection Zone – Dee the first designated WPZ

Monitoring silt and mud movements, cliff erosion and water depths

Marine Protected Areas (MPAs) – areas of the ocean set aside for long term conservation aims. MPAs support climate change adaption and migration while providing other ecosystem services.

Dee Regulation System – protecting communities further downstream from severe flooding; flood defence measures to protect Wirral and Welsh coastline and banks

RNLI Hoylake established in 1803 and HN Coastguard Flint, safety surveillance and rescue services for estuary recreational users and fishing workforce

Airborne early warning and control system (AWACs) to monitor effluent emissions

Control of all construction methods to achieve target of zero for temperature increases

Conservation control of streets, paths, trees and views including de-forestation checks

Joint Nature Conservation Committee JNCC

Ramsar convention for Wetlands and Natura 2000 EU ecological protection

The Dee Estuary European Maritime Site 2010; Sensitive Marine Area (SMA)

Biodiversity Audit Project BAP – integration with estuary management partnerships

Protection from farm and sewer discharges and plastic to protect global oceans

Global protection of rivers and oceans – Rights of Nature

ClimateEarth (CE) and Friends of the Earth (FoE) presently suing UK Government after COP26 since no legal strategy in place to end fossil fuel cars and gas boilers.

CONCLUSION

From Industrial to Green Revolution

Cotton and Coal were the prime motivators of the Industrial Revolution. The major engineering event on the Wirral peninsular was the coal mining industry at Neston which operated from 1759 to 1928. This is illustrated by the fact that in 1801 the village of Birkenhead had a population of only 110 compared to Greater Neston at that time with a population of 1,486. In many areas the evolution of mining was to have a tremendous impact on construction, canal works and railway industries.

The Institution of Civil Engineers (ICE) was formed in 1828 and at that time a Durham civil and railway engineer, Thomas Tredgold, provided a definition of civil engineering which was adopted by the Institution. (This is presently under review by ICE following the Johannesburg Summit of Sustainable Development of 2003):

the art of working with the great sources of power in nature
for the use and convenience of man

In the main, engineering skills were applied by the owners of industry to increase their financial benefits but very little of this was used to improve the conditions of their workers. Britain in 1828 was still the time of serfdom with most working people having no rights of employment and education. This also applied to women and children. Five years later the Slavery Abolition Act was passed, however Poor Laws were introduced with workhouses penalising poor people and often separating children from their parents. Many more years were to pass before working families were to be given their democratic voting rights. Religion provided some comfort and protection but in general the church authorities took the side of the Government.

The working and living conditions of miners at Neston fell well below a civilised standard, as was the case for many coalfields in England, Wales, Scotland and Ireland. In particular the hardship of working down mines for women and small children was a lasting scandal associated with the British government's disregard of this injustice during the eighteenth and nineteenth centuries. Miners were treated as 'slaves'.

Some of the deaths and serious injuries suffered by young and elderly mine workers were recorded but before 1800 many mining authorities did not even pay the respect of any record of these injustices, written or otherwise. This remains the case today in many of the poorer countries around the world. British governments and their industrial authorities were blind to the suffering caused by their working practices carried out during the Industrial Revolution.

In their book, *Between Extremes* published in 1999, Brian Keenan and John McCarthy, who were imprisoned for four years in a Lebanese dungeon, described the victims of the mines in Chile, left in old age with amputated limbs, having great difficulty in breathing, and barely existing without provision of social care. The search for coal has a grim record of slavery, especially for young children working down mines. This was also true for young children working in mills or sweeping chimneys.

History shows that engineers and scientists have applied their ingenuity to solving man's immediate problems but often with little thought regarding side effects such as pollution and disease. This applied to the works carried out on the River Dee and its estuary. The health of our planet has greatly suffered mainly inflicted by the richer nations during the industrial revolutions. There is an inextricable link between the present climate emergency, biodiversity and human health.

Starting in 2019, a Welsh coastal monitoring team has been analysing data which will predict the most effective location for constructing sea defence walls. The past and current erosion of parts of the estuary banks are also being taken into account.

Jim Hall, Professor of climate and environmental risk at Oxford University's Environmental Change Institute, has been monitoring the rising sea levels. Also, a US-based climate change research group Climate Central has predicted that part of Merseyside will be an area of the UK which will be underwater by 2050.

Also during recent years schemes have been set in place allowing under-productive land to 're-wild', that is go back to nature. Re-forestation should include the re-planting of hedgerows. In Wales one out of six wildlife species is at risk of extinction. There are present debates on carbon-offsetting, the reduction or removal of carbon dioxide or other greenhouse gases in order to compensate for polluting emissions elsewhere. Wirral Council is now encouraging children's travel to school by walking and cycling. Children's early introduction to exercise also helps their long-term health.

The story of the farmer's daughter who set out to bring back her father's cattle from the marshes, was recorded by Charles Kingsley in his poem, 'The Sands of Dee'. She lost her life as the mist descended and the wind whipped up the waves into a storm; her remains were recovered by the local boatmen the next day. There had been previous drownings of local people especially where farmers had grazed cattle on the estuary. The Dee had enacted its powers on other than miners' children.

Survival was the primary motive for humans' initial existence on our planet, and has now come full circle to today's potential global catastrophe. Upstream carelessness has downstream consequences. Care and attention to pollution, in order to counter climate change, may still save our planet. It is not too late for us to retrieve some of the damage already inflicted on our planet and this will require all sections of humanity to contribute to this global effort, but especially the need for the more secure nations to support the more vulnerable.

Water is an essential element of life and cannot be taken for granted. Oceans are a huge body of saltwater that cover more than 70 per cent of the Earth and more than 80 per cent of oceans remain unexplored. There is the opportunity for the world to apply all its resources on the basis of co-operation and to stop the unnecessary conflicts which are presently absorbing so much wasted effort and time, injury and loss of life. Britain presently produces more carbon in two days than the Democratic Republic of Congo produces in one year. The UN needs to have the power to ensure the timetable against global pollution is maintained.

A local initiative on climate change was reported by the *Wirral Globe* newspaper on 18 May 2022:

> Three years after declaring a climate emergency, Wirral Council has received international recognition for its commitment to carbon reduction.
>
> The council has achieved bronze status as a 'Carbon Literate Organisation', awarded by the Carbon Literacy Trust, and becomes the first authority in Merseyside to do so.

As children we were told to get on with the job – 'don't stick your head in the sand'.

The 'sands of time' are running out!

APPENDIX

United Nations Sustainable Development

The United Nations is an Intergovernmental Organisation which was founded in 1945 to maintain international peace, security and friendly relations between nations.

The UN Sustainable Development Goals (SDGs) were set up in 2015 by the UN General Assembly to be achieved by 2030. The 17 goals are as follows:

No poverty

Zero hunger

Good health and well-being

Quality Education

Gender Equality

Clean Water and Sanitation

Affordable and clean energy

Decent work and economic growth

Industry, innovation and infrastructure

Reduced inequalities

Sustainable inequalities

Responsible consumption and production

Climate action

Life below water

Life on land

Peace, justice and strong industries

Partnership for the goals

The UN recognised that ending poverty and other deprivations must go hand-in-hand with strategies that improve health and education, reduce inequality and spur economic growth – all while tackling climate change and working to preserve our oceans and forests.

APPENDIX

Climate Change and future Green Environment

The Intergovernmental Panel on Climate Change (IPCC)

Two decades ago the United Nations Framework Convention on Climate Change (UNFCCC) first identified the need for intergovernmental action. The climate change scientists have now concluded that man's behaviour since the time of the industrial revolutions has caused carbon emissions [the carbon footprint] raising the global temperature by about 1.1°C with serious implications for our planet's survival.

In 2015 at Paris an IPCC agreement was reached to strengthen the global response to the threat of climate change by 'holding the increase in the global average temperature to 1.5° Centigrade above pre-industrial levels'.

Bio-diversity is the engine that produces everything we consume. There has been degrading by man of wildlife including loss of habitats. In Britain the wildlife in great danger of extinction are Scottish wildcats, natterjack toads, turtle doves and hedgehogs. UK has only half of its entire bio-diversity left since the Industrial Revolution, and is in the bottom 10 per cent of the world's countries, globally below the planet's 'safe level'. Survival of plants depend on the spread of seeds by animals.

During the Industrial Revolution, coal was critical in powering new industries but this is now identified as the major contribution to global warming by increasing carbon dioxide emissions. Over the last 200 years the average world temperature has risen by 1°C. In 2020 governments under UN direction agreed on a target limiting rise in temperature by 1.5°C by 2050. It is likely that global rises in ocean levels will significantly affect silting of the River Dee and estuary. In addition flooding events due to global warming of nearby landmasses and woodland loss need our attention.

COP26 (2021 UN Climate Change Conference)

The United Kingdom Government has recently been in discussions with other governments to agree actions to counter climate changes likely to have extreme global impact on our planet. The main category of study, inspection and control relates to stabilising carbon dioxide emissions by means of an agreed coordinated global plan of action, and its execution need to be closely monitored (including de-carbonising).

This action plan supervised by the United Nations is to be devolved internationally. The national governments are then to sub-divide these responsibilities into localised action areas. Annual climate reports will provide the basis for closer cooperation, world safety and peace. International research will include technological advances in use of power sources, heating choices [green hydrogen and heat pumps] identifying most vulnerable areas (nations' equity gap) requiring special measures of assistance.

Carbon Offsetting and Carbon Capture need to be scrutinised as legitimate carbon reduction proposals. Elimination of fossil fuels, re-foresting, reduced air travel, electric vehicles, house insulation, and meat & dairy reduction are important contributions.

Forests keep down global temperatures by forming a carbon sponge, transforming energy and water and keeping the climate stable.

However, Clean Energy Revolution currently highlights workers' poor conditions in cobalt mining in the Democratic Republic of Congo for electric vehicle batteries.

APPENDIX

Climate Change Threat to Coastal Areas

The University of St Andrews has carried out recent research on the vulnerability of coastal regions to the threat posed by Climate Change. Victoria Gill states that the coastal saltmarsh is 'engineered to fight climate change' by locking in carbon emissions into the mud bed.

Skinflats RSPB Reserve near Falkirk was restored in 2018 noting following points:

Wetland mud could ease climate change

Ocean's climate change 'buffer' is under threat

Letting sea come in over saltmarsh is called 'blue carbon' which is stored in coastal and marine ecosystems such as tidal marshes and seagrass meadows. Blue carbon is stored naturally through plant growth and the accumulation and burial of organic matter in the soil or mud. Coastal salt marshes are very efficient at absorbing large quantities of greenhouse gas carbon dioxide from the atmosphere.

However Natural Resources Wales (NRW) have stated protecting all areas was 'difficult against the forces of nature'. This challenge applies to the coastline surrounding the Dee estuary. To reduce greenhouse gas emissions (carbon dioxide and methane) there is a need to increase rates of re-cycling of waste and to lower rates of waste incineration in order to meet the zero emissions target in 2050.

During Cop26 in November 2021, pledges were sought from all participating governments (200 countries signed up to the Glasgow Climate Pact) on:

Reduction of methane, coal, transport and de-forestation

Other items under consideration:

heat pumps, storage wells and planting trees – carbon capture (CCS)

renewable energy offsets – solar, wind and hydro sites

re-cycling, insulation – reduction of carbon footprint

The UK has already initiated two projects in the North of England:

Humber and Teeside East Coast Cluster – potential to capture, transport and store up to 27m tonnes of CO2 emissions a year by 2030.

Hynet North West Project in Liverpool Bay – carbon hydrogen from fossil gas

Climate Change Committee (**CCC**) – net-zero by October 2021

However globally, low level areas like the Virgin Islands in the Caribbean are likely to be soon submerged in water and will require immediate assistance to cope with increasing ocean flooding. Can global finance step up to the net-zero challenge – if only for self-interest – a new alliance of financial institutions must recognise the need to avert a global climate catastrophe.

Six years ago in Paris, countries reached a historic agreement to limit global temp rise to less than 2C targeting 1.5°C. Since then there has been only limited investment in decarbonisation. Public pressure especially from younger generations is starting to make the difference. Pressure on resources for health emergencies has to be resolved.

Kelly Sheehan, Senior Director of Energy Campaigns for the Sierra Club – reducing 'FF' is the only way to stop being vulnerable to the whims of greedy industries and geoplitics (based on 2022 report that US intend to provide natural gas to EU).

APPENDIX

Epidemics and Pandemics through the Ages

The World Health Organisation (WHO) is a specialized agency of the United Nations responsible for international health which was founded in 1948.

Viruses, epidemics and pandemics are recurring features of human history. Most of these originated in large populations where poverty and lack of clean water were endemic. Their effect on Britain and Ireland were as follows:

Eleventh century

A Leprosy pandemic started in the Middle Ages requiring the urgent building of hospitals to cope with the vast number of victims. It was considered God's punishment. At Spital near Poulton on the Wirral, a hospital for 'lepers' was recorded in 1283.

1347–50 [first outbreak in Europe but earlier plague outbreaks]

The Black Death was a wasting disease responsible for the death of half of the world's population as the second largest outbreak of Bubonic Plague started in Asia moving west. The British feudal system collapsed when the plague changed economic circumstances. The Vikings lost strength to wage battle against native populations.

1640–70 Plagues and Great Plague

A Pestilence affected every part of Europe (Chester 1654). The Great Plague of London was on a smaller scale to the Black Death resulting in 75,000 deaths. This was followed by Smallpox from the late sixteenth century to the late nineteenth century.

Main Victorian diseases

Consumption (Tuberculosis TB) killed 1 in 7 of all people.

Keats, Chopin, Bronte sisters and Grace Darling died from consumption.

Dr Joseph Lisster (Father of antiseptic surgery) developed an antispetic between 1877 and 1893.

Other Victorian diseases:

Gout, scarlet fever, whooping cough

1817–1866

Cholera started on the Indian subcontinent in 1817 with seven pandemics over the next 150 years. It entered Britain by the port of Sunderland in 1831 spreading to Scotland and reached London by 1832, with further outbreaks in 1852 and 1866.

1830

Typhus (fever) started with worst outbreak during 1837–38; also during the Great Irish Famine 1846–49. Alexander I of Russia died of typhus in 1825 and Anne Frank died of typhus in a concentration camp in 1944.

Date 430 BC–1940s

Typhoid (fever) recorded before Roman times. Prince Albert died of typhoid in 1861.

1918–1919

Spanish Flu globally 500 million people or one third of the world's population died; cases recorded in Chester and North Wales.

1920–90

AIDS at least 35 million died until medication developed in the 1990s.

2019–present

WHO announced that the first case of Covid-19 was reported in China on 17 November 2019 before it became a global pandemic. by 11 March 2020.

The *Lancet* (Countdown) in Oct 2021 reported on climate change in the context of COVID 19 pandemic:

> effect on mental and physical health contributes to spread of infectious diseases
>
> productivity of various food sections including agriculture, forestry and fishery sections exacerbating food security

These types of serious health issues require continuing resarch, monitoring and measures available for immediate application and response.

APPENDIX

Dee Estuary/Current Waters and Industries

Wirral Waters

The reduction of flow in the River Dee and Dee Estuary is partly due to the fact that the Rivers Severn and Mersey no longer flow into the Dee. Most streams and drains flow eastwards into the River Mersey estuary. Streams draining into Mersey include:

Caldy Brook	
Wallasey Pool	Arrowe Brook-Greasby Brook, Caldy Brook
Birket	Fender-Prenton Brook
Tranmere Pool	
Plymyard Dale	
Bromborough Pool	Dibbinsdale
Raby Vale, Hargrave Brook	
Eastham	
Hooton Pool	Whitby Brook
Sutton Brook	
Shotwick Brook	
Stanney Brook	
River Gowy	Thornton Brook

Fishing Industries

Cockling beds – West Kirby & Thurstaston (2no) and North Wales (7no)

Regulation – issues with sustainability – licences checked by police

Strong tidal currents and shifting sands giving dangerous conditions

Other fishing subject to licence. Includes plaice, Dover sole and skate.

Dee Estuary Cruising
3 buoyed channels: 1) Welsh Channel 2) Mid Hoyle Channel 3) Hilbre Swash

Wirral Dee Coastal Industries
Ellesmere Port Ince power stations ceased operations 1997;

Stanlow oil refinery (Essar Oil UK)

Capenhurst uranium enrichment plant

Recent records include discharges at Meols and West Kirby Marine Lake

North Wales Waters
Reservoirs in the upper part of catchment store water and regulate flow into Dee.

The Environment Agency (and Natural Resources Wales) are responsible for the management of the environment and natural resources of the catchment.

North Wales Dee Coastal Industries
Underground coal gasification in the Dee estuary on hold

Point of Ayr natural gas sweetening plant; Point of Ayr wind towers

Mostyn Tidal Lagoon – commercial docks

Chemical manufacturing plant – hydrogen ready boilers (A55)

Treated sewerage effluent from Queensferry works and Chester

Commercial docks at Mostyn – tide limited works

St Asaph Wind Farm substation and heat pumps

Connah's Quay – port for Buckley brickworks and gas-fired power station

Connah's Quay – measuring gas from Irish Sea well (DRS group)
            1993 1420 MW gas-fired power station.
            (1954 old station coal-fired – coal from Point of Ayr colliery.)

Deeside Power Station (CCGT) – 1 mile east of Connah's Quay

Flint – alkali works, fuels, chemical building blocks

Shotton Steel Works closed 1980, now areas previously occupied by power station and paper mills, and reservoirs converted to nature reserves

Liverpool Bay Hydrogen Development (HyNet)

APPENDIX

Military and Recreational Facilities

MoD Firing Range (established during WWII)

In 2004 RAF Sealand closed and was taken over by MOD Sealand. The Sealand Rifle Ranges manages 486 hectares at the Burton marshes on the Dee estuary for the MOD.

Rail, Bus, Walking, Running, Cycling and Horse-riding

The former Chester to Hoylake Railway (surveyed by G. Stephenson in 1830, opened in 1837 and closed by Dr Beeching in 1966) was re-developed as the Wirral Way & Country Park for use by walkers, cyclists and horse riders. In addition it provides landscape views of the Dee estuary and the North Wales hills. There is a donkey sanctuary at Bristage near Barnston.

Sailing, Surfing and Swimming

The Marine Lake at West Kirby was first built in 1897. In 2009 the lake was refurbished and now provides facilities for sailboarding, sailing and kayaking to international standards. Swimming and surfing facilities are also available. New sea defence wall proposals for West Kirby presently under consideration.

Ellesmere Port Canal and canal linkages around Chester including the Shropshire Union Canal, Chester Canal, Bridgewater Canal, Trent & Mersey and Macclesfield Canal. UK's canals and navigational rivers are managed by navigation authorities who are responsible for their maintenance; the largest authorities are the Canal & River Trust and the Environment Agency.

Fishing

The River Dee and Dee Estuary provide fishing for salmon, trout and shell fish. NRA and EA have been appointed to the management of the Dee Estuary cockle fishery. By the early 1900s shrimp fishing in the estuary was carried out at Heswall; silting up of the estuary had forced a move from Parkgate.

Golf

There are many golf courses located adjacent to the Dee coastline including those at Hoylake and West Kirby, Thurstaston and Heswall.

Football and Rugby

The first football club on the Wirral founded in 1884 was Tranmere Rovers (Old Norse Trani-meir) near Birkenhead. The first rugby club located between Neston and Bromborough was founded in 1936.

Bird Watching and Wildlife

Burton Mere Wetlands is recognised as a major centre for bird-watching and wildlife especially bird waders and wildfowl. There are also nature reserves extending around the perimeter of the estuary. The Hilbre islands are also well known for wildlife including birds, seals, voles and land mammals, foxes, hedgehogs, crabs, fish species, shore invertebrate animals, red beadlet anemones and seaweed.

Hunting and Shooting

Only certain species of game birds, quarry birds and waterfowl can be shot during shooting season, subject to licence. There is currently a campaign to stop trail (fox) hunting. Badgers and their setts are protected (WCBG).

APPENDIX

Silting, Erosion and Pollution on the Dee

Upper Reaches

From the source of the River Dee springs on the slopes of Dduallt above Llanuwchllyn in the mountains of Snowdonia to its emergence from the Vale of Llangollen. Here the young river flows swiftly and the majority of river erosion takes place by cutting relatively narrow steep-sided 'V'-shaped valleys'.

Middle Reaches

Through England and the Welsh borders to Chester the 'middle-aged' river slows down and the valley becomes broader. Both erosion and deposition of material takes place, leading to the formation of meanders and occasional changes of course which have in places left pockets of England 'stranded' on the Welsh side of the River Dee.

Siltation

Silt is a solid, dust-like sediment that water, ice and wind, transport and deposit. Silt is made up of rock and mineral particles that are larger than clay but smaller than sand.

Silt increases the potential for flooding.

Water polluted closely with sediment prevents animals from seeking food. Sediment deposits in rivers can alter the flow of water and reduce depth making navigation and recreational use more difficult. River flows determine how much sediment it can erode depending on river slope, volume of flow, and shape of stream bed.

During stormy events, the winds blowing across an estuary cause sediment to be carried by 'whipping', resulting in backflows. Estuary habitat loss can be as high as 60 per cent, and this affects fish and shellfish.

Estuaries naturally filter water; as water flows through wetlands such as saltmarshes much of sediment and pollutants are filtered out.

Pollution

Pollution is the introduction of harmful materials into an environment. Pollution can be caused by air, light, litter, noise, plastic, soil, radioactive material, thermal action, water (including sewage), and visual effects such as landfill, litter, fumes and plastic. Meanwhile 80 per cent of ocean pollution (marine pollution) migrates onto sides of estuary and inland. Chemicals, nutrients, and heavy metals can travel out to sea.

Air pollutants include ozone 03, nitrogen dioxide NO2, carbon monoxide CO, sulphur dioxide SO2; particulate matter includes PM10 and PM2

Silt pollution from building sites can deoxygenate the water, block gills of fish, smother aquatic plants, starve invertebrates of light and oxygen; however silt deposits can enrich agriculture. Nature is always in a state of balance.

Wetland management are presently searching for plant species to reduce microbial methane production. Methane has more than 80 times the warming power of carbon dioxide over the first twenty years after it reaches the atmosphere.

Dee Estuarine Silting and Saltmarshes

The Dee water has never been sufficient to scour out an adequate navigation channel through the deep glacial silt. In more recent centuries, man has contributed to the silting up of the Dee. At one time the Dee Mills, owned by the earls of Chester, operated eleven waterwheels and also constructed a weir across the river at Chester, which reduced the tidal limit and the scour of the river. It is also possible that upland deforestation in Wales altered drainage patterns and also contributed to the silting. The majority of coastal salt-marsh in the Dee estuary is between Parkgate and Heswall.

Farming management needs to ensure the maintenance of healthy soil and grassland and biodiversity. Few of the Wirral saltmarshes are grazed.

Other estuarine silting may have included the extraction of water into the canals during the 'canal mania' period of history. This led to the reclamation of land which could then be sold, but did not assist the improvement of the port of Chester.

Burton Mere Wetlands (established 2011)

This is a nature reserve on the Dee estuary straddling the border between Cheshire and Flintshire. It is run by the RSPB (from 1983) and incorporates the older Inner Marsh Farm Reserve. The area contains a wide variety of wildlife. In 1922 a saltmarsh grass called Spartina was introduced to stabilise the sand and mudflats of the reclaimed land; by 1952 this grass had colonised the Parkgate sands and now has spread in certain coastal areas further north.

Sealand

This is an area in Flintshire and on the south west edge of the Wirral. At earlier times the Mersey may have flowed through into the Dee in what is now called Sealand, by means of a channel which cut through the base of the peninsular.

North Wales Nature Reserve

The RSPB also supervises the Point of Ayr Dee Estuary Nature Reserve (Flintshire) and along the Welsh side of the estuary from Chester to Point of Ayr.

Radioactive pollution from the sea

Recent research has been carried out on discharge of radioactive waste into the sea off Cumberland coast from nuclear power station at Sellafield. This discharge amounts to 2 million gallons of radioactive water into the Irish Sea every day at high tide. This has caused the Irish Sea to be the most radioactive contaminated sea in the world.

Breeding Birds

Many birds travel long distances to and from Wirral's Dee Estuary as one of their northern breeding grounds. These birds include the knot, ringed plover, curlew, redshank, oyster-catcher, grey plover, bar-tailed godwit, sanderling, and dunlin. Pedestrians are warned to keep their dogs under control so as not to disturb these birds during the breeding months September to March.

The survival of insects is essential to the survival of birds and animals, this includes water stick insects. This is closely linked to many aspects of climate warming. Biodiversity also depends on insects, espeically bees.

APPENDIX

Wirral – Bird Watching and Climate Change

Ref September 2000 [waders]

Burton Mere Wetland

[great egret], [black-tailed godwit], [spotted redshank], [wood sandpiper], willow warbler, [spoonbill], [long-billed dowitcher], whinchat, [little stint], hobby spotted flycatcher, bittern, merlin, grey wagtail, wheatcar, marsh harrier, [spoonbill], green woodpecker, long-tailed dowitcher

Hilbre, Middle-Eye & Tansky Rocks

[hoopoe], medodious, garnet, jouivide rock pipit, [curlew sandpiper], [little stint],

[little egret], peregrine, wheatear, [curlew], [oystercatcher], [dunlin], [sandwich tern]

Leasowe Lighthouse

tree pipit, whinchat, blackcap, chiffchaff

Moreton

[green sandpiper]

Parkgate

marsh harrier, spoonbill, [curlew sandpiper], ruff, hobby, little-ringed plover, swallow, [pink-footed geese], short-eared owl

Heswall Shore

[redshank], common gull, [little egret], [grey heron], shelduck, marsh harrier, ringed plover, [oystercatcher], ringed plover, grey plover, [greenshank], black-headed gull

Meols Shore

juvenile Mediterranean gull, [little egret], [arctic skua], whimbrel

Connah's Quay Nature Resort

merlin, [greenshank], [redshank], [black-tailed godwit], [great egret], [spoonbill]

Arrow Park Lake

kingfisher

New Brighton

[dark-bellied brent goose]

Hoylake Shore

American golden plover, [sandwich tern], [roseate tern], red kite

Pensby

common redstart

West Kirby & Caldy

[summer plumaged turnstone], [sandwich tern]; [black-tailed godwit]

Thurstaston

mediteranean gull, shelduck, [oystercatcher], [black-tailed godwit], [curlew], [redshank]

Bromborough & Willaston

siskens; hobby

Decca Pools (near Denhall Quay)

hen harrier, red kite

Ledsham

spotted flycatcher

Bird numbers for most species during the Covid-19 pandemic have shown a significant decrease. This is an important indicator of Climate Change.

Climate Change is affecting European birds due to rising temperatures – fewer chicks and eggs.

The world's birds can be described as: the planet's 'canaries in the coalmine' used for detecting a potential catastrophe.

North West England link to Ireland

The history of the Dee and Ireland has been linked over 2000 years. In AD 79 the Romans made a vital decision to establish a base in Chester and not to invade Ireland, but 800 years after the Romans left Britain, the Anglo-Normans invaded Ireland. Initially it was in response to the request for help by the Irish King of Leinster, Diarmuid MacMurrough, but then King Henry feared that 'Strongbow', the second earl of Pembroke, would set up an independent Kingdom in Ireland. This could affect control of the Irish Sea and present a threat to England's security. Thereafter for nearly 700 years the English rulers kept Ireland under subjugation.

Ireland's history has been dominated by poverty and epidemics, which has forced many Irish people to migrate to other countries for temporary work, or on a permanent basis.

The arrival of the Vikings on Wirral in AD 900 was the first direct involvement of the Irish Norsemen on Wirral soil and surrounding coastal areas. Some Vikings made the Wirral a permanent settlement; the remaining Vikings returned to Dublin in 914.

During the Middle Ages English activity in Ireland was subdued but in 1372 a postal service was established between Chester and Dublin. The British govermnent considered that reliable connections were still important.

The arrival of the Tudors and Elizabethans began a further period of military action in Ireland. During the reign of Elizabeth I the plantation of Ireland started, and for the next fifty years Chester's trade other than cloth was 'manifestly decayed'.

By 1603, the start of the Pre-Industrial Revolution, Neston Old Quay was still the main outport for Chester. In 1609 the plantation of Ulster started. The Royalist troops from Ireland landed at Mostyn in 1643 and Chester was in a state of war for two years. Cromwell's invasion of Ireland (1649–50) resulted in a 'massacre' of the Irish. William III in 1689 departed from Hoylake with Protestant troops for his battle with James II in Ireland. Parkgate became the main outport for Chester especially for Dublin from 1685. After the construction of the New Cut to provide an improved channel on the Welsh side of the Dee estuary in 1737, increased trade was facilitated between Chester and North Wales as well as continental ports and Ireland.

The first Industrial Revolution started in 1760 with the slave trade centred on Liverpool. At the failure of the Irish Rebellion in 1798 many Irish escaped to Britain. Chester was no longer the chief port of North West England. In 1815 the continuing silting of the

Dee estuary resulted in the last ferry sailing from Parkgate. Coal continued to be exported from Denhall Quay to Ireland and the Isle of Man.

During the second Industrial Revolution the export of coal to Ireland continued, including the use of the old quay at Neston and the anchorage at Dawpool. Liverpool was now established as the main port. The start of the Potato Famine in the mid-1840s resulted in a surge of migrants from Ireland to Liverpool. Many migrants sought work in the neighbouring districts around Liverpool such as the Wirral. The railway and canal construction brought in many Irish navvies to England and Scotland seeking work.

In 1867 Fenians attacked Chester Castle in order to obtain arms for a rising in Ireland. This attempt ended in total failure.

During the battle for Independence in Ireland from 1916 to 1922 there were many military ships taking troop reinforcements to Ireland, and then during the civil war following until the Irish Constitution was founded in 1937. The separation of Northern Ireland was to remain a matter of bitter dispute.

APPENDIX

Famous Engineers

The greater number of early engineers were the offspring of necessity.

What were England without its roads, its bridges, its canals, its docks, and its harbours. What were it without its tools, its machinery, its steam-engine, its steam-ships, and its locomotives.

[T]he Locomotive was invented, and all that Telford had done was, to a certain extent, undone by the Stephensons.

Samuel Smiles 1864

Scottish Engineers

Thomas Telford (1757–1834) born Dumfriesshire

An engineer, architect and stonemason; known as 'Colossus of Roads', builder of 1000 miles of roads, 1000 bridges, 40 docks and numerous canals, and appointed County Surveyor of Shropshire in 1786, and designer of Llangollen Canal in 1806.

Telford was Engineer for the Ellesmere Canal in 1791 (Ellesmere and Chester canals were amalgamated in 1813); Telford and Jessop were responsible for the Pontcysyllte Canal during 1795 to 1805. The Shropshire Union Canal was his last major project.

His outstanding achievements are the design and construction of the Menai Bridge (1819–26), Caledonian Canal (1804–22) and Runcorn Bridge in 1814. He was responsible for improving the roads from Cheshire and Shrewsbury to Holyhead, the main route to Ireland. He was founder and first President of the Institution of Civil Engineers in 1828.

John Rennie (1761–1821) born East Lothian

Started working on canals in London area, then in north of England followed by the Kennet & Avon Canal and extensive drainage projects. In Dublin he supervised canal and harbour works. After various bridge works, he designed a lighthouse for Glasgow. He was a pioneer in the use of structural steel.

James Watt (1736–1819) born Greenock

An instrument maker at Glasgow University he then became a leading inventor of steam engines, a mechanical engineer and chemist. His major achievement was the improvement of the Newcomen's 1712 steam engine. Watt surveyed the Caledonian Canal in 1773. He entered a partnership with businessman Matthew Boulton in 1777; the firm Boulton and Watt became eventually highly successful in the use of steam engines. He developed the concept of 'horsepower' and the unit of power, the 'watt'.

Robert Stevenson (1772–1850) born Glasgow

Civil engineer and famed as a designer and builder of lighthouses. Even at the age of 19, he was given the responsibility for the Bell Rock lighthouse which was based on the Eddystone lighthouse. He made a tour in 1801 of the Wirral lighthouses (built at Leasowe and Bidston in 1763 and 1771) for assisting ships entering Liverpool. The Point of Ayr lighthouses were constructed in 1776 and 1818. His grandson was author Robert Louis Stevenson. In 1828 he made tour of north Wirral with William Laird. His grandson was author Robert Louis Stevenson.

North East England Engineers

George Stephenson (1781–1848) Newcastle upon Tyne

Known as the 'Father of Railways' for his involvement in many of the early rail projects. In 1815 he was responsible for the first locomotive at a Newcastle colliery, first steam locomotive at Stockton & Darlington Railway in 1825 and principal engineer for first inter-city railway line between Manchester and Liverpool in 1830.

He was responsible for the sinking of a number of coal mines, and invented a miner's safety lamp nicknamed the 'Geordie'.

Robert Stephenson (1803–59) Newcastle upon Tyne

Son of George Stephenson was born in Wallsend (east end of Hadrian's Wall). He had an early training in railway design and was considered the greatest engineer of the nineteeth century. With his father he was involved in the survey for a railway to transport coal from Bishop Auckland mines to Stockton. He then spent three years in South America, first at Colombian mines followed by harbour works in Venezuela up to 1827. After designing the locomotive 'Rocket' for the Manchester to Liverpool Railway, he managed the steam locomotive factory at Newcastle with William Howe pattern maker and inventor of the link motion system to steam engine in 1842.

John Buddle (1773–1843) born Stanley Co Durham

A self-made mining engineer and entrepreneur in North East England. He had a major influence on the development of the Northern Coalfield in the first half of the nine- teenth century, He also became a shipowner, and was in charge of the building of Seaham

Harbour. He was promoted to viewer (manager) of Benwell Colliery. In 1835 he was intimately involved in the testing of the Davy safety lamp.

Nicholas Woods (1795–1865) born Ryton Co Durham

Colliery and steam locomotive engineer; he promoted mining safety. He became the President of the North of England Institute of Mechanical Engineers. He started as an apprentice colliery viewer under the supervision of viewer Ralph Dodds (surveyor of canals and coal mines); Woods became manager of Killingworth Colliery in 1815. He became a close associate of colliery enginewright George Stephenson.

Joseph Cabry (1773–1858) born Tanfield Co Durham

In 1818 at Burradon Colliery in Northumberland, Joseph Cabry, a friend and fellow engineer of George Stephenson, who mentioned that the steam engine at Neston was 'working satisfactorily'. In 1819 George Stephenson was in communication with Joseph Cabry as an Engineer and a publican at the Wheatsheaf pub in Neston. This was copied to Robert Stephenson and to Joseph's son Thomas who was also working at Neston Colliery.

Ralph Pearson (1718 Gateshead) and Matthew Bates (1828 Gosforth)

Both 'engineers' were from North East coal mining families who were particularly skilled and experienced in sinking shafts down to coal seams. These pit sinkers were considered to be the 'elite' of coal miners.

South West and North/Midlands English Engineers

Thomas Newcomen (1664–1729) Dartmouth, Devon

An ironmonger by trade from Cornwall, he created the atmospheric engine, the first practical fuel-burning engine in 1712. Working on the ideas of Cornishman Thomas Savery and French born physicist Denis Papin he created a steam engine for lifting water out of a tin mine. Two years later the Newcomen engine was demonstrated at a number of Yorkshire and Flintshire collieries including at Hawarden. Between 1715 and 1778 a large number of Newcomen steam engines were used in the collieries around Newcastle upon Tyne. Another Cornish inventor Richard Trevithick in 1805 designed a lighter locomotive for the Newcastle collieries.

Humphrey Davy (1778–1829) Penzance, Cornwall

Sir Humphry Davy from Penzance inn Cornwall, scientist, inventor and President of the Royal Society was well known in all British coalfields for the Davy lamp. In 1815 following explosions at a number of Newcastle collieries, he devised his safety lamp to safeguard lighting in mines with methane or 'fiery' environments.

James Brindley (1716–72) Derbyshire

He worked on the design and construction of water wheels to produce power to grind corn and for similar purposes. He was a pioneer in the provision of canal engineering working on the earliest canals in the modern era. In 1761 in collaboration with the 3rd Duke of Bridgewater, his proposals for an underground canal from Worsley Brook to the junction with the River Irwell near Manchester, avoided the need for a large number of lock gates. In 1763 he installed a steam engine (manufactured at Coalbrookdale) at Walker Colliery near Newcastle upon Tyne. Brindley was also involved in the design of the Chester Canal.

William Jessop (1745-1814) Plymouth Devon

In 1791 Jessop (a pupil of John Smeaton) proposed a scheme for connecting Ellesmere Canal to join the Mersey with the Dee at Chester. He had previously considered a canal connection of Wirral with Wrexham.

Thomas Brassey (1805–1870) Cheshire, William MacKenzie (1794 Nelson Lancs)

They were civil engineering contractors; Brassey was also a materials manufacturer at Birkenhead and responsible for building of most of the world's railways, including the railway line in Ukraine during the Crimean War. Associated with most of the railway works, he controlled the building of many stations including Chester Station. The River Dee is crossed by the Cefn Maur Viaduct built in 1848 by Thomas Brassey.

Basil Mott (1858–1938) Leicestershire

He was a notable civil engineer who rose to a respected position as a consulting engineer in many fields of construction with Mott Hay & Anderson. In 1874 Neston Colliery Co. intended to purchase mineral rights to land in Little Neston from Sir Charles Grey Mott director of the Great Western Railway. In 1885 Basil Mott designed an underground haulage system including the construction of three tunnels. In 1924 Basil Mott was appointed President of the Institution of Civil Engineers.

Engineers – Past, Present and Future

During the early nineteenth century George and Rawling Stott were mineral boring engineers from Ferryhill in County Durham who won a reputation for this field of engineering. By the use of preliminary boring techniques to determine the location and nature of the coal seams in advance of pit sinking, this avoided waste of resources and time.

Currently Professor Peter Stott is a leading climate scientist who has emphasised the importance of governments to commit resources to achieving climate change targets. The title of his recent publication includes the words 'Battle against Climate Change'. The change in direction of political and commercial interests will certainly be a battle, but could encourage countries to work together, and it will be necessary for engineers to play an essential contribution, especially in the field of infrastructure. Otherwise a catastrophe of gigantic proportions will result.

In the next thirty years it will be essential that scientists, engineers, and governments worldwide work in close partnership to carry out works which will reduce the effect of emissions of carbon dioxide and methane. The dangers of high temperatures, burning forests, rising sea levels and flooding will require close planning and implementation of emergency resources to protect and move to safety, vulnerable members of the population. It is ironical that the poorest countries who contributed least to climate change are now most at risk to food shortages, water insecurity and displacement of populations. The *Guardian & Observer* charity appeal 2021 has highlighted that 'poorer nations are paying the price for wealthy nations' pollution'.

The December 2021 edition of the magazine New Civil Engineer reflects that civil engineers' focus is now very much directed on the issue of Climate Change. The editor even scrutinised the decisions made by Government on HS2 in view of the conclusions of the recent COP26 climate conference. Also emphasis was given to subnational leaders having a crucial role in delivering 'net zero'. This applies to the full scope of engineering including contractors, consultants and designers. The new President of the Institution of Civil Engineers, Ed McCann, highlighted the critical nature of the work civil engineers can do to mitigate and manage the climate crisis.

It is now reported that the famous consulting engineers Arup Group Ltd are to stop taking work on non-renewable energy projects. Arup have said that they will not pursue work on any new energy projects that support the extraction, refinement or transport of hydrocarbon-based fuel. They state that they are committed to undertaking whole life carbon assessments for all of their building projects – new and retrofit – from 2022. As in the past engineers will need to be observant of future indicators which will need early planning and action on infrastructure works. Future pandemics and environment changes will require fundamental changes in nations' ways of working and living.

Bibliography

Ancestry.com, Census Records UK

Anderson, V. R., *The Chester & Holyhead Railway* (1969)

Annakin-Smith, A., *Neston Collieries Trail* (Ellesmere Port & Neston Borough Council 2009)

Annakin-Smith, A., *The Neston Collieries, 1759-1855: An Industrial Revolution In Rural Cheshire* (University of Chester Press 2019)

Annakin-Smith, A., *The Canals that Almost Came to Neston* (2019)

Annakin-Smith A., *The Neston Collieries 1875-1927: What happened When* (2021)

Anthony, Andrew, 'England's crumbling coasts amid climate crisis' (*The Observer* Jan. 2022)

Armour, C., *The Trade of Chester and State of the Dee Navigation 1600–1800* (University of London, 1955)

Atkinson, Keith, *History of Shotton – Deeside: The River Dee & Latchcraft Pits* (John Summers & Sons 2009)

Barkham, Patrick, 'Should rivers have the same rights as people' (*The Guardian* July 2021)

BBC Liverpool, 'Blood, Sweat and Tears in Neston' (November 2014)

Bidston Lighthouse Stevenson Archives (2017)

Blake, Brian, *The Solway Firth* (Robert Hale, 1956)

Bowes, Virginia, *St Winefride's Roman Catholic Church* (1993)

British History Chester Economy and Society 1662–1762, *Roman Chester*

Burnley, Kenneth, *Portrait of Wirral* (Robert Hale Ltd)

Burton, Anthony, *The Canal Builders* (Pen & Sword Book Ltd, 1972)

Carey, Brycchan, 'Beilby Porteous Biography' (MacMillan 2005)

Carrington, Damion, 'Net-zero climate strategy – UK Government' (*Guardian*, Jan 2022)

Carter, Richard, *The Iniquity of Oblivion, Quakers graves, Burton Woods* (2013)

Chappell, Gavin, *Smugglers of Parkgate and Heswall* (Countyvise June 2009)

Challinor, R., *The Lancashire and Cheshire Miners* (Newcastle upon Tyne 1972)

Chester wikipedia, 'History of Chester River Dee' (June 2021)

Cheshirenow, 'The Guide to Cheshire, Derbyshire, Lancashire and Wirral' (Medieval Cheshire 2006)

Chesterwiki, 'Middle and Lower Reaches' (July 2021)

Chesterwiki, 'AEthelflaed daughter of Alfred the Great' (Nov 2021)

Chrimes, Michael, *The civil engineering of Canals and Railways before 1850* (Ashgate Publishing Group 1998)

Chrimes, Mike, 'William Jessop's canal proposals' (2002)

Clarke, Angela, *Parkgate Society Newsletter* (no 93, 2017)

Clark, Jo, *Chester Historic Towns Survey* (HTS Chester District 2003)

Construction News, 'Thomas Telford's 250 year legacy' (Sept 2017)

Copernicus Sentinel-5P, 'Satellite night radar monitoring methane emissions' (March 2022)

Dawson, Greg, 'Coal Mining in Wirral' (*Heswall Magazine* June 2017)

Dawson, Greg, 'How the port of Chester cost Heswall and Parkgate their sandy beaches' (*Heswall Magazine* April 2018)

Dee Estuary News, 'The Dee Estuary and the 20th Century' (Nov 1999)

Devine, Vince & Dolman, Michael, *Neston Archaeological Assessment Hydrogen Development in Wales* (Elementenergy December 2020)

Douglas, David D., *The Age of the Normans* (T. Nelson & Sons Ltd 1969)

Engineering Timeline, 'Newcomen Engines at Hawarden' (1997)

Engineering data, 'Dee Estuary Bathing Water Profile' (2021)

English Heritage, 'Archaeological Assessment' (Cheshire County Council, 2003)

Environment Agency, 'The Dee Management Catchment summary' (2012)

Environment Agency, 'The Dee Protection flood risk assessment' (2018)

Errington, Anthony, *Coal on Rails* (Liverpool University Press 1825)

Fflint.co.uk/industry, 'Industry through the Ages: A Study of the history of Flint with photographs' (2021)

Foster, Eric, *The Pit Children* (Blackwells 1978)

France, Peter, *Roman roads in Wirral, Neston & Parkgate Remembered: How were the mines worked* (1986)

Galloway, R. L., *A History of Coal Mining in Great Britain* (David & Charles 1969)

Gill, Victoria, 'Coastal saltmarsh engineered to fight climate change' (BBC News Science correspondence Nov 2021)

Google Maps, Gaergwrie Wrexham (2021)

Green, Roger L., *Myths of the Norsemen* (Puffin 1994)

Halcrow Engineers, 'Dee Estuaries Report' (2013)

Halliday, Stephenson, 'Archaeological and historic context: Connah's Quay Solar Farm Heritage Impact Statement'

Harding, Stephen, *Viking Mersey Scandinavian Wirral, West Lancashire and Chester* (2002)

Harding, Prof Steve, 'Viking Wirral – and Viking Genes' (*Heswall Magazine* February 2010)

Higginbotham, Peter, *Workhouses: Wirral, Cheshire* (2021)

Hillditch, Edward, *A short history of Neston and Surrounding Villages* (The Burton & Neston History Society Dec 2018)

Hindley, Meister, *Merchants of Liverpool, Roman Roads in Cheshire* (2021)

Hutchinson, S. M., *Siltation in the Saltmarsh of the Dee Estuary*

Isle of Man.com, *The Great Duke of Bridgewater* (Lancashire Worthies Dec 2018)

Prandle, D., 'Cs Analysis of Shallow Cores' (Liverpool University 1993)

JNCC, 'Dee Estuary (Aber Dyfrdwy) designated SAC salt meadows'

JNCC, 'Coastal Saltmarsh biodiversity' (Joint National Conservation Committee Colin Wells 1991)

Jowitt, Prof. P. W., 'Sustainability and the formation of the civil engineer' (Proceedings of the Institution of Civil Engineers June 2004)

Kelly, Helena, 'Heritage Impact Statement' (Aug 2019)

Kingsley, Charles, *Alton Locke Tailor and Poet An Autobiography* (Walter Scott, London 1850)

Kingsley, Charles, 'The Sands of Dee' (Poetry by Heart)

Liverpool.ac.uk, 'Dee Wrecks Dawpool' (2021)

Lloyd, G., 'The Canalisation of the River Dee'

McRonald, Jenny, 'Heswall History'

Lane, Roger, (Heswall Magazine 2017)

Lees, Alexander, 'Broad decline in bird population' (Manchester Metropolitan University 2022)

Mason, Peter Ford, *The Pit Sinkers of Northumberland and Durham* (The History Press 2012)

Mason, Peter Ford, *James Shannon: The Journey of an Irish family AD812–1886* (Scotforth Books 2015)

Mason, Peter Ford, *Pit-Lad Paddy* (Austin McCauley 2021)

Merry Sights, 'The Wirral, Parkgate, Neston, Willaston and Burton'

Mines and Collieries Act 1842

1842 commissioners mine sketches – stock photos

Michael, Charles D., *The Slave and his champions* (S. W. Partridge & Co London 1891)

Michael, Chris, 'Wrecks in the Dee Estuary' (wrecks/wrDee/html 2021)

Morgan, Jennifer, 'A test for humanity, a time for action', Greenpeace International Executive Director 29/10/21

Naturiol, Cyfoeth, 'Marine Character Areas Dee Estuary' (Wales) Cymru Natural Resources Wales MCA 01

National Oceanography Centre, 'The River Dee – About Tides' (2021)

Natural England, 'Regarding Beach Management: Advice to Wirral Council' (April 2020)

Nat Resources Wales (EA), The Dee River basin District (RBD) (Dee prelim flood risk assessment Dec 2018)

NRA Welsh Region, 'The NRA's Vision for the Dee Catchment' (July 1994)

Nelson, Gwyn, 'Prediction of factors effecting sea wall locations' (Wales Coastal Monitoring Team 2019)

Neston Parish Church, 'Neston Parish Church / History' (2021)

Neston Past.Com, 'Neston and its Collieries' (2018)

Neston Town Council, 'Timeline for CH64' (2021)2

Neston Town Council, 'Emma, Lady Hamilton' (26 April 1765 – 15 January 1815)

Neston Pictorial, 'A Photographic History (of Parkgate)' monologues.co.uk

New Civil Engineer, 'Defining civil engineering' (NCE 2018)

New Civil Engineer, 'Second National Infrastructure Assessment' (2021)

New York Times, 'Cobalt mining in Democratic Republic of Congo' (Nov 2021)

Palmer, William T., *The Verge of Wales* (Robert Hale Ltd: London, 1943)

Parkgate Society, 'Parkgate Origins History' (2021)

Passmore, Alan, *The Railway at Parkgate, The Chester & Holyhead Railway* (Burton & Neston History Society 1984)

Pearson, Jeffrey, *Neston & Parkgate Remembered* (Countyvise 1998)

Pencheon, Prof David, 'Climate Change/COVID 19 pandemic' (The *Lancet* Countdown Oct 2021)

Peres, Prof. Carlos, 'Climate change risks disruption of seed and pollen transport' (University of East Anglia January 2022)

Philpott, Dr Robert, 'Cheshire Shore Projects' (Merseyside Archaeological Society, 1991)

Place, Geoffrey, *Neston 1840–1940* (Burton, South Wirral local history society)

Place, Geoffrey, 'The Repatriation of Irish Vagrants from Cheshire' (*Journal of Chester Archaeological Society* 1986)

Purvis, Andy, 'Conference UN Bio-diversity COP26'

Quaglin, Sofia, Climate Change/Birds (National Academy of Sciences, 2022)

Ratledge, David, 'The Roman Road from Chester to the Wirral' (Roman Roads Research Association)

Rideout, E. H., *Wirral Watersheds and River Systems and their Influence on local history* (Historic Society Lancs & Cheshire 1922)

Rideout, Edna, *Wirral Watersheds and River Systems and their influence on local history* (1922)

Rideout, Edna, *The Chester Companies and the Old Quay* (History Society Lancashire & Cheshire 1927)

RSPB, 'Burton Mere Wetlands' (Dan Trotman Nov 2016)

Saint Exupery, Antoine de, 'Global Warning of 1.5 C' (IPCC special report 1948)

Sealand community council, *A History of Sealand – the community that rose from the sea* (Sealand community council 2021)

Sharma, Simon, *Rough Crossing, Britain, the Slaves and the American Revolution* (BBC Books, 2005)

Sheehan, Kelly, 'Protection of Environment, Social Change' (Sierra Club, March 2022/ *Guardian*)

Shropshire Union, 'Holiday Guide' (Sept 2021)

Skempton, A. W., *Biographical Dictionary of Civil Engineers*

Smiles, Samuel, *James Brindley and the early Engineers* (John Murray London 1864)

Smiles, Samuel, *Lives of the Engineers, George and Robert Stephenson* (John Murray Albemarle Street London 1904)

Stephenson, Halliday, 'Connah's Quay Solar Farm' (PAC Report Nov 2019)

Stevenson, Robert, *Wasting Effect of the Sea on the shore of Cheshire between the rivers Mersey and Dee* (February 1828)

Stott, Prof. Peter A., *Hot Air: The Inside Story of the Battle against Climate Change Denial* (Atlantic Books)

Swift, Roger, *Irish Migrants in Britain* (Cork University Press 2002)

Taylor, M. William, *River Dee Bridge Disaster 1847: Iron Engineering and Architectural History in Crisis* (2021)

Trotman, Dan, 'The Joy of Counting – Dee Estuary' The RSPB Community (2021)

Wikipedia, 'William Davenport slave trader' (2021)

Wikipedia, 'Roman Roads in Britannia' (2021)

Wikipedia, 'History of Chester' (July 2021)

Wikipedia, 'Sealand, Flintshire' (Aug 2021)

Woodward, D. M., *The Overseas trade of Chester 1600–1650* (University of Hull 1970)

Woods, Cuthbert E., *Smuggling in Wirral* (Historical Society of Lancs & Cheshire 1927)

The Wytchery, 'The Sands of Dee' (Charles Kingsley, 1849) Gothichorrorstories.com (2021)

UN Food/Agric Organisation, 'Plastic threatening food and Health safety' (*The Guardian* 07 December 2021)

Index